KT-177-820

LADY MARGARET HALL LIBRARY
OXFORD
F&1153

302210269P

OROGRAPHICAL
FEATURES
OF THE
BRITISH ISLES

ALTITUDE TINTS

0 Feet   200   400   1200   2000 Feet

SHETLAND
ISLANDS

ORKNEY
ISLANDS

CAITHN.

CHANNEL
ISLANDS

ISLES
OF
SCILLY

ISLE OF MAN

O.R. 1860

3,000/10/51 S.P.C., R.E.

War Office 1951.

M.O. 488

AIR MINISTRY

METEOROLOGICAL OFFICE

CLIMATOLOGICAL
ATLAS
OF THE
BRITISH ISLES

LONDON: HER MAJESTY'S STATIONERY OFFICE
1952

Decimal Index
551. 582. 3(41/2).

Crown Copyright Reserved

PUBLISHED BY HER MAJESTY'S STATIONERY OFFICE

To be purchased from

York House, Kingsway, LONDON, W.C.2   423 Oxford Street, LONDON, W.1
P.O. Box 569, LONDON, S.E.1

13a Castle Street, EDINBURGH, 2   1 St. Andrew's Crescent, CARDIFF
39 King Street, MANCHESTER, 2   Tower Lane, BRISTOL, 1
2 Edmund Street, BIRMINGHAM, 3   80 Chichester Street, BELFAST

or from any Bookseller

1952

Price £2 12s 6d net

Printed in Great Britain under the authority of Her Majesty's Stationery Office

By Multi Machine Plates Limited

26/2/51 W/S 7170-Wt4911-K24-G21-961.   S.O. Code No. 40-148*

PREFACE

The preparation of a Climatological Atlas of the British Isles was begun in 1938 but had to be suspended on the outbreak of war.

The original lay-out of the Atlas was agreed with the various interested Governmental Authorities. When the work was resumed in 1945 the National Agricultural Advisory Council emphasized the importance of an atlas of this kind for the development of agriculture in Great Britain, and, on the Council's recommendation, additional information has been compiled and maps prepared for inclusion in the Atlas.

Most of the maps show the average conditions for the thirty-year period 1901-1930. This period was selected by the International Meteorological Organization as the standard period for climatological averages for all the meteorological services of the world. As comparable observations for some elements such as visibility and cloud did not begin so early as 1901, data for later periods covering as many years as possible have been substituted.

Much of the material used in preparing this Atlas has been provided by the numerous voluntary observers throughout the British Isles who have maintained meteorological stations or rain-gauges for many years ; without their co-operation and accurate work it would not have been possible to produce the Atlas in its present detail.

NELSON K. JOHNSON
Director

CONTENTS

LIST OF PLATES

GENERAL INTRODUCTION

Climate may be defined as the summation of weather over a long period of years. The climate of any region is the most important and fundamental natural influence upon the way of life of its inhabitants, its animals, and its vegetation. In all human communities, whether thick or sparse, climate determines all matters concerning the three main necessities of life : food, clothing and shelter.

A reference book on the climate of any particular region is therefore a requisite for all proper planning for the welfare of its inhabitants, and the most convenient form in which climatic facts can be presented is that of an atlas, which shows clearly and concisely the distribution geographically of the various weather elements which go to make climate.

This " Climatological Atlas of the British Isles " is the result of the collection of weather data over many years. It is based on the co-operative efforts of many thousands of climatological observers, who recorded observations at one or more prescribed times every day of the year. Some of the contributing climatological stations were maintained by the Meteorological Office itself and some by Local Authorities or other interested bodies. There were also many stations which owed their existence to the enthusiasm of voluntary observers, to whom British climatology is greatly indebted.

The present volume is the first reasonably complete climatological atlas of the British Isles to be published. Its predecessors were the charts of day and night temperature, amount of rainfall and duration of bright sunshine published in the " Book of normals of meteorological elements "[1]*; the " Rainfall atlas of the British Isles "[2]; and the maps of relative humidity and vapour pressure in "Averages of humidity for the British Isles "[3]. Excellent descriptions of the distribution of the climatic elements have been given by Bilham[4].

The atlas is divided into ten sections, each of which deals with one of the climatological elements. The arrangement of the sections is as follows :—

1. Pressure.
2. Wind.
3. Temperature.
4. Rainfall.
5. Snow.
6. Thunder.
7. Humidity.
8. Sunshine.
9. Fog and Visibility.
10. Cloud.

Details of the maps and diagrams in each section are given in the List of Plates.

Each section is complete in itself. It has its own introduction, in which are described briefly the methods of making observations and correcting the data, when necessary, for the preparation of the plates. For full details, however, of the observational routine, reference should be made to the " Meteorological observer's handbook "[5], of which one edition or other was the text-book for all the observers concerned. Some introductions also include tables or diagrams to supplement the plates. Following the introduction are given, here and there, interesting items concerning extreme values or comparison between long-period statistics. In all sections (except Section 10) information about the plates is then given, and there follows a bibliography consisting of a numbered list of the papers referred to in the preceding text and references to the more important literature dealing with the subject of the section.

---

* The superior figures refer to the bibliography on page 3.

Regarding the maps : some elements, notably atmospheric pressure, mean temperature and relative humidity, show in the details of their distribution so close a relation to configuration that isopleths of the values at " station level " would closely follow the contours.   In order to bring out the underlying broadscale distribution, these elements have been " reduced to mean sea level " by the application of appropriate corrections, which are set out in the respective introductions.   The value expected at any given height can be found quite simply by applying the appropriate correction to the reduced value, with the sign reversed.   In other cases, such as extremes of temperature, amount of rainfall, and wind speed, the distribution bears a relation to configuration which is less exact, and the introduction of a correction would confuse rather than simplify the maps.   For such elements the maps show the distribution at the level of the station in as much detail as the scale allows.

The maps are based on Clarke's spheroid.   On the one-page map the scale along parallel 54° is 1 in 4·13 million, and along a meridian it is 1 in 4·24 million.   The quarter-page maps are in proportion.

A detailed orographical map of the British Isles forms the frontispiece.   The other maps show only the outline of the coast, the latitude and longitude, the principal rivers and the major features of the topography.   The distribution of each element is superimposed in bold lines, and in most instances is further emphasized by colour-shading in standard colours, thus—brown for pressure and visibility, red for temperature, green for humidity, blue for precipitation and orange for sunshine.   A map showing the location of the observatories and stations mentioned in the atlas will be found at page 4, and a gazetteer at page 5.

The word " average ", rather than " normal ", has been used throughout this atlas.   The period 1901-1930 has been adopted as a standard one for climatological " normals " by the International Meteorological Organization, and wherever possible the data used in constructing the maps of average conditions refer to this same period 1901-1930.   But observations have not been made for the full period at some stations, even of pressure and temperature, and for other elements, such as visibility and cloud, the records cover a shorter time at all stations.   The term " average " was therefore adopted to describe all means over a period of years.

The climate of a country is not represented by its averages alone ; extreme conditions are also important.   These are represented by maps of the extremes of temperature and wind velocity, by maps of the distribution of pressure and rainfall on selected days, and by graphs of the frequency of values between various limits.

Another important characteristic of the climate is the diurnal variation.   Hourly values of all meteorological elements have been taken regularly at the four observatories maintained by the Meteorological Office at Aberdeen, Eskdalemuir, Kew and Valentia.   From these records hourly means for each alternate month have been computed, in most cases for the 30 years 1901-1930, and these values are shown as graphs.   In addition the diurnal variation is shown for selected days—*e.g.* a very hot day, a humid day.

Unless it is otherwise stated, all times quoted refer to Greenwich Mean Time.

Definitions of the days referred to are given in the text.   They are usually climatological days from 9h. to 9h., but are occasionally civil days, midnight to midnight.

The months are the calendar months January to December.

The seasons are as follows :—

Spring	...	...	March 1-May 31.
Summer	...	...	June 1-August 31.
Autumn	...	...	September 1-November 30.
Winter	...	...	December 1-February 28 or 29.

The year is the calendar year January 1-December 31.

GENERAL REFERENCES

The principal publications in which weather data for the British Isles appear are as follows :—

British Rainfall Organization ; *British rainfall*, 1860-1918.

Edinburgh, Scottish Meteorological Society ; *Journal*, 1866-1921.

Greenwich Royal Observatory ; *Results of the magnetical and meteorological observations made at the Royal Observatory, Greenwich*, 1836-1936.

Liverpool Observatory ; *Report of the Liverpool Observatory*, 1851-.

London, Meteorological Office ; *Quarterly weather report*, 1869-1880.

London, Meteorological Office ; *Meteorological observations at stations of the second order*, 1876-1910.

‡London, Meteorological Office ; *Weekly weather report*, 1878-.

London, Meteorological Office ; *Hourly readings*, 1881-1886, 1900-1910.

‡London, Meteorological Office ; *Monthly weather report*, 1884-.

London, Meteorological Office ; *Annual summary of the monthly weather report*, 1905-.

London, Meteorological Office ; *Hourly means*, 1887-1899.

London, Meteorological Office ; *British meteorological year book*, 1908-1910.

London, Meteorological Office ; *British meteorological and magnetic year book*, 1911-1921.

London, Meteorological Office ; *British rainfall*, 1919-.

London, Meteorological Office ; *Observatories' year book*, 1922-1937.

London, Meteorological Office ; *Monthly frequency tables*, 1927-.

London, Meteorological Society ; *The meteorological record*, 1881-1882.

London, Royal Meteorological Society ; *The meteorological record*, 1883-1911.

Oxford, Radcliffe Observatory ; *Results of the meteorological observations made at the Radcliffe Observatory, Oxford*, 1854-.

SHAW, SIR NAPIER and AUSTIN, E. E. ; Manual of meteorology. Cambridge (Cambridge University Press), 1926.

Southport, Fernley Observatory ; *Report and results of observations by Joseph Baxendall*, 1892-1917.

Southport, Auxiliary Observatory ; *Annual report and results of meteorological observations for the year*, 1918-.

Stonyhurst College Observatory ; *Results of meteorological, magnetical and seismological observations*, 1860-1943.

Data from these publications have been widely used in the preparation of this atlas. In addition, other published records or summaries have been used to complete some of the maps ; such sources are acknowledged in the bibliographies of the sections concerned.

The maps, diagrams, and tables also incorporate much information which has not been published : this exists as manuscript records in the possession of the Meteorological Office, being the original returns, on the appropriate forms, from the observatories and stations.

BIBLIOGRAPHY

[1] London, Meteorological Office. The book of normals of meteorological elements for the British Isles for periods ending 1915. Section III, Maps of the normal distribution of temperature, rainfall and sunshine. London, 1920.

[2] Royal Meteorological Society. Rainfall atlas of the British Isles. London, 1926.

[3] London, Meteorological Office. Averages of humidity for the British Isles. London, 1938.

[4] BILHAM, E. G. ; The climate of the British Isles. London (Macmillan), 1938.

[5] London, Meteorological Office. Meteorological observer's handbook. London, 1942.

---

‡ These publications were included in the *British meteorological and magnetic year books* for the period 1911-1921.

4

OBSERVATORIES
AND
STATIONS MENTIONED
IN THE ATLAS

London Area Reference			
1	Greenwich	7	Epsom
2	Enfield	8	Kenley
3	Croydon	9	S. Kensington
4	Addington Hills	10	Camden Square
5	Hornchurch	11	Byfleet
6	Northolt	12	Biggin Hill

War Office 1950

GAZETTEER OF STATIONS MENTIONED IN THE ATLAS

The approximate positions of these stations are shown on the map opposite.

Station	Lat. N. ° '	Long. ° '	Station	Lat. N. ° '	Long. ° '	Station	Lat. N. ° '	Long. ° '
Abbotsinch (Glasgow)	55 52	4 26W.	Enfield	51 40	0 10W.	Paisley	55 51	4 26W.
Aberdeen	57 10	2 06W.	Epsom	51 20	0 16W.	Peebles	55 39	3 12W.
Aberystwyth	52 25	4 04W.	Eskdalemuir	55 19	3 12W.	Pembroke Dock	51 42	4 57W.
Abingdon	51 41	1 19W.	Exmouth	50 36	3 24W.	Penrhos	52 52	4 28W.
Addington Hills (Res.)	51 22	0 04W.	Falmouth (Observatory)	50 09	5 05W.	Penzance	50 07	5 32W.
Aisholt	51 07	3 09W.	Falmouth (Pendennis Castle)	50 09	5 03W.	Point of Ayre	54 25	4 22W.
Aldergrove	54 39	6 13W.	Felixstowe	51 57	1 20E.	Portland Bill	50 32	2 27W.
Alness	57 41	4 15W.	Fleetwood	53 56	3 01W.	Plymouth (Mt. Batten)	50 22	4 07W.
Ashburton	50 31	3 45W.	Fort William	56 49	5 07W.	Princetown	50 33	3 59W.
Aviemore	57 11	3 50W.	Glasgow	55 52	4 17W.	Raunds	52 20	0 31W.
Balerno	55 52	3 21W.	Glenquoich	57 04	5 16W.	Redcar	54 37	1 04W.
Ballynahinch Castle	53 27	9 53W.	Gordon Castle	57 37	3 05W.	Renfrew	55 52	4 24W.
Balmakewan	56 48	2 33W.	Gorleston	52 35	1 43E.	Rhayader	52 11	3 31W.
Balmoral	57 02	3 12W.	Great Gable	54 28	3 13W.	Rhondda	51 39	3 29W.
Barnstaple	51 05	4 03W.	Greenwich	51 29	0 0	Rhyl	53 19	3 29W.
Bawtry	53 26	1 01W.	Halstead	51 57	0 38E.	Rickmansworth	51 39	0 29W.
Bellingham	55 13	2 18W.	Hallington Fawcett	55 04	2 03W.	Ross-on-Wye	51 55	2 35W.
Bell Rock	56 26	2 24W.	Harford	50 25	3 54W.	Rothamsted	51 48	0 22W.
Ben Nevis	56 48	5 0W.	Hartland Point	51 01	4 32W.	Rotherham	53 25	1 19W.
Bidston (Liverpool Observatory)	53 24	3 04W.	Hastings	50 51	0 34E.	St. Abb's Head	55 55	2 08W.
Biggin Hill	51 19	0 02E.	Haverfordwest	51 48	4 58W.	St. Ann's Head	51 41	5 10W.
Bingley	53 51	1 51W.	Haywards Heath	51 01	0 06W.	St. Athan	51 25	3 25W.
Bircham Newton	52 52	0 40E.	Hemswell	53 24	0 34W.	St. Eval	50 28	4 59W.
Birmingham (Edgbaston)	52 29	1 56W.	Holyhead	53 19	4 37W.	Scampton	53 18	0 32W.
Birr Castle	53 06	7 56W.	Hornchurch	51 32	0 13E.	Scarborough	54 17	0 24W.
Blackadder	55 47	2 14W.	Huddersfield (Oakes)	53 39	1 50W.	Scilly	49 56	6 18W.
Blackpool	53 49	3 03W.	Hull	53 45	0 16W.	Seaforde	54 18	5 51W.
Blacksod Point	54 06	10 04W.	Ivybridge	50 23	3 55W.	Seaham Harbour	54 51	1 19W.
Boghall	55 52	3 12W.	Jersey (St. Helier)	49 11	2 06W.	Sealand	53 13	3 0W.
Borrowdale	54 31	3 09W.	Kelso	55 36	2 25W.	Seaton	50 42	3 04W.
Boscombe Down	51 10	1 45W.	Kenley	51 18	0 05W.	Seathwaite	54 30	3 11W.
Boston	52 58	0 0	Kensington (London)	51 30	0 10W.	Sellafield	54 25	3 31W.
Braemar	57 0	3 24W.	Keswick	54 36	3 09W.	Shoeburyness	51 32	0 49E.
Bristol (Whitchurch)	51 25	2 35W.	Kew	51 28	0 19W.	South Farnborough	51 17	0 45W.
Bruton	51 07	2 27W.	Kilmarnock	55 37	4 29W.	Southport (Fernley Observatory)	53 39	2 59W.
Butt of Lewis	58 31	6 16W.	Kinlochquoich	57 03	5 21W.	South Shields	55 0	1 26W.
Buxton	53 16	1 55W.	Kirkwall	58 59	2 57W.	Spurn Head	53 35	0 07E.
Byfleet	51 17	0 26W.	Larkhill	51 11	1 48W.	Squires Gate	53 46	3 02W.
Calshot	50 49	1 18W.	Leicester	52 38	1 05W.	Stirling	56 07	3 56W.
Camden Square (London)	51 33	0 08W.	Lerwick	60 08	1 11W.	Stonyhurst	53 51	2 28W.
Cambridge	52 12	0 08E.	Leuchars	56 23	2 53W.	Stornoway	58 11	6 21W.
Cannington	51 09	3 04W.	Lewes	50 52	0 01E.	Strontian	56 41	5 34W.
Canterbury	51 17	1 05E.	Leyburn	54 19	1 49W.	Sullom	60 26	1 15W.
Cantref	51 50	3 27W.	Linton-on-Ouse	54 03	1 15W.	Sutton Bonnington	52 50	1 15W.
Cardiff	51 28	3 10W.	Liverpool Observatory	53 24	3 04W.	Tangmere	50 51	0 43W.
Cardington	52 07	0 25W.	Lizard Head	49 57	5 12W.	Thornaby	54 32	1 18W.
Carluke	55 45	3 53W.	Logie Coldstone	57 08	2 55W.	Thorney Island	50 49	0 56W.
Castleton	54 28	0 56W.	Lossiemouth	57 43	3 20W.	Tintagel	50 40	4 45W.
Catterick	54 22	1 37W.	Lympne	51 05	1 01E.	Tiree	56 29	6 52W.
Church Fenton	53 50	1 12W.	Malin Head	55 23	7 24W.	Tonbridge	51 12	0 16E.
Colwyn Bay	53 16	3 44W.	Manchester (Barton)	53 28	2 23W.	Torquay	50 28	3 31W.
Cranwell	53 02	0 30W.	Manston	51 21	1 22E.	Tunbridge Wells	51 08	0 16E.
Crieff	56 22	3 50W.	Marchmont House	55 44	2 25W.	Turnhouse	55 57	3 21W.
Croydon	51 21	0 07W.	Markree Castle	54 11	8 27W.	Tynemouth	55 01	1 25W.
Cullompton	50 51	3 23W.	Market Drayton	52 55	2 24W.	Upper Heyford	51 56	1 15W.
Dalwhinnie	56 56	4 14W.	Meltham	53 36	1 50W.	Valentia	51 56	10 15W.
Darwen	53 41	2 28W.	Middlesbrough	54 35	1 14W.	Wakefield	53 40	1 30W.
Deerness	58 56	2 45W.	Mildenhall	52 22	0 28E.	Wakehurst	51 03	0 05W.
Detling	51 18	0 36E.	Montrose	56 44	2 28W.	Walton-on-the-Naze	51 51	1 16E.
Digby	53 05	0 24W.	Moreton Hampstead	50 39	3 46W.	Weaver Point	51 48	8 17W.
Douglas	54 10	4 28W.	Mursley	51 59	0 49W.	West Calder	55 51	3 34W.
Dover	51 07	1 19E.	Newton Rigg	54 40	2 49W.	West Linton	55 45	3 21W.
Driffield	54 0	0 28W.	North Coates	53 29	0 02E.	Wick	58 27	3 05W.
Dublin	53 20	6 15W.	Northolt	51 33	0 25W.	Wigtown	54 52	4 27W.
Dunfanaghy Road	55 11	7 58W.	North Weald	51 43	0 14E.	Winchelsea	50 56	0 43E.
Dun Fell	54 41	2 27W.	Nottingham	52 56	1 09W.	Windermere	54 23	2 55W.
Dungavel	55 37	4 08W.	Oban	56 25	5 29W.	Wolfelee	55 23	2 39W.
Dungeness	50 55	0 58E.	Ochtertyre	56 23	3 54W.	Worthy Down	51 07	1 19W.
Durham	54 46	1 35W.	Omagh	54 36	7 19W.	Wyton	52 21	0 07W.
Duxford	52 05	0 08E.	Oxford (Radcliffe Observatory)	51 46	1 16W.	Yarmouth	52 37	1 43E.
Eallabus	55 47	6 14W.						
Eastbourne	50 46	0 17E.						
Edinburgh	55 55	3 11W.						

§1—PRESSURE

INTRODUCTION

The maps of barometric pressure are based on observations made with mercury barometers. All observations were corrected at the time for the temperature of the attached thermometer and were reduced to mean sea level and normal gravity for latitude 45°. Details of these corrections are given in the " Meteorological observer's handbook "[1]*. The unit of pressure used was the millibar (mb.). Conversion to millibars of pressures read on barometers graduated in inches was effected by taking 1000 millibars as equal to the pressure exerted by a column of mercury 29·5306 inches high under the standard conditions of temperature (mercury at 32°F., barometer scale at 62°F.) and a value of gravity equal to 980·617 centimetres per second per second.

HISTORICAL BACKGROUND

(a) Extremes of Pressure

Table I gives, for each calendar month, the highest and lowest mean sea level pressures known to have been recorded at official stations making observations at one or more fixed hours a day. It is of course possible that pressures exceeding these limits have occurred at other hours at these stations but have not been recorded.

TABLE I.—EXTREMES OF PRESSURE

	Jan.	Feb.	Mar.	Apr.	May	June	July	Aug.	Sept.	Oct.	Nov.	Dec.
Highest (mb.) ...	1055	1050	1045	1045	1042	1034	1038	1032	1039	1039	1044	1050
Lowest (mb.) ...	925	951	948	953	968	977	976	968	971	947	940	927

The highest pressure of 1054·7 mb. was recorded at Aberdeen on January 31, 1902, and the lowest, 925·5 mb., at Ochtertyre, Perthshire, on January 26, 1884.

(b) Long-period Changes of Pressure Distribution

It is of interest to compare the averages of pressure for 1856-1895 compiled by Buchan[2] with those for 1901-1930 which are used as the basis of the maps in this section. The figures are given in Table II.

TABLE II.—COMPARISON OF PRESSURE AVERAGES

		Jan.	Feb.	Mar.	Apr.	May	June	July	Aug.	Sept.	Oct.	Nov.	Dec.	Year
							1000 mb. *plus*							
Lerwick														
1856-1895	...	6·0	9·0	8·3	12·5	13·8	13·7	11·1	10·1	9·6	7·8	7·9	6·1	9·6
1901-1930	...	5·8	6·8	7·6	10·0	13·8	13·5	12·3	9·5	12·1	8·7	6·3	3·7	9·2
Scilly														
1856-1895	...	14·7	15·5	13·7	13·6	15·2	17·1	15·7	15·0	15·2	12·9	13·2	14·7	14·7
1901-1930	...	16·5	14·2	13·0	14·0	15·3	17·5	16·9	15·7	17·1	13·3	13·6	12·3	14·9
Valentia														
1856-1895	...	11·8	14·1	13·1	13·1	14·5	16·4	15·1	14·5	14·3	11·9	13·3	13·2	13·8
1901-1930	...	13·7	12·2	12·1	13·9	14·8	17·1	16·1	14·4	16·3	11·8	12·6	10·1	13·8
London														
1856-1895	...	16·1	16·7	13·7	14·3	15·5	16·7	15·5	14·9	15·9	13·2	14·2	15·5	15·2
1901-1930	...	16·9	15·0	12·9	13·4	15·6	16·8	15·9	14·9	17·2	14·2	13·9	12·6	14·9

The most noteworthy feature is the lower pressure at Lerwick in each of the months from November to April during the second period.

* The superior figures refer to the bibliography on page 9.

PLATES 1-5

MAPS OF AVERAGE MONTHLY AND ANNUAL MEANS OF DAILY PRESSURE, 1901-1930.—The maps show the average daily pressure by isobars at 1-mb. intervals. The maps are based on figures obtained from a variety of sources, mainly manuscript records for stations published in the *Monthly weather report*, but also from the *Journal* of the Scottish Meteorological Society for 1901-1919, *The meteorological record* of the Royal Meteorological Society for 1901-1911, and from the publications of various observatories.

Observations were taken at various hours, mainly 7, 8 or 9h., or 9 and 21h. All means have been corrected to the mean of 24 hours. For this to be done, monthly maps were constructed from all available hourly data, and the corrections required to reduce means at 7, 9, 13 and 21h. to the 24-hour mean determined. The stations used for this were Lerwick, Aberdeen, Fort William, Glasgow, Eskdalemuir, Oxford, Kew, Falmouth, Valentia and Jersey. In addition, the corrections for 7 and 13h. were computed for Stornoway, Spurn Head, Holyhead, St. Ann's Head, Malin Head and Blacksod Point, using as a basis ten-year averages of observations at 1, 7, 13 and 18h. with a small approximate correction to the mean of 24 hours. These corrections were examined for consistency in relation to neighbouring months and smoothed where necessary. After this they were included in the means of 24 hours plotted on the maps.

To prepare the maps of average pressure, data for 81 stations were extracted for as much as possible of the period 1901-1930. Short gaps in the records for any particular station were completed by the interpolation of values obtained from neighbouring stations. Then for each station the averages were formed for as many as possible of the five-year periods 1901-1905, 1906-1910, etc. Missing five-year period averages were then interpolated by comparison with neighbouring stations, and thus 30-year normals were obtained for each of the 81 stations.

The average annual values were plotted first, and smooth isobars for each 0·2 mb. were drawn. Some values failed to fit these smooth isobars exactly, and these were examined. In some cases a small systematic error was discovered which accounted for the inconsistency : at some coastal stations showing anomalous values the effect of wind was suspected, but for others no explanation could be found. In all such cases a correction was estimated from the map of annual values and this was applied to the monthly values.

The corrected average monthly means were then plotted, and on the same maps the resultant winds, calculated from anemograph records, were also plotted. The isobars were drawn to agree with the plotted average pressures, details of the distribution being verified from the winds. A notable example is the southward bend of the isobar over south-east Kent which appears on the map for the year and on those for several of the months ; this is fully supported by the winds.

CHARTS OF PRESSURE DISTRIBUTION ON TYPICAL DAYS.—The average pressure distributions shown on Plates 1-4 were derived in effect from hundreds of pressure patterns for individual hours, known as " synoptic charts." These synoptic charts were constructed for at least four fixed hours per day and used for forecasting the weather. The pressure patterns on synoptic charts take a great variety of forms, as can be seen from a study of the *Daily weather report*[3], but most of them are variations from a few simple types. Five of these recognized types have been selected from the charts published in the *Daily weather report*, as follows :—

A *depression*, or region of low barometric pressure, generally accompanied by strong winds and rain.

A *secondary depression*, or low pressure system accompanying a larger primary depression, and giving similar weather.

A *trough of low pressure* (formerly known as a *V-shaped depression*), usually accompanying the passage of a well marked " front."

An *anticyclone*, or region of high barometric pressure, generally accompanied by light winds and fine weather in summer, by fog and frost in winter.

A *wedge* of high pressure between two depressions, giving a transient period of settled weather.

Explanation of the Weather Maps.†

Pressure. Isobars are drawn for every 4 millibars. The region of lowest pressure is indicated by the word " Low," that of highest pressure by the word " High."

Wind. The arrows fly with the wind. A full-length feather indicates two steps and a short feather one step on the Beaufort scale of wind force. (See Table I of Section 2—Wind.) Calm is indicated by a circle.

Temperature is given in degrees Fahrenheit.

Weather. The letters, according to the Beaufort notation[4], used to indicate the weather at the station at the time of observation are :—

Beaufort Letter	Description	Beaufort Letter	Description	Beaufort Letter	Description
b	blue sky	h	hail	r	rain
c	cloudy	m	mist	rs	sleet
d	drizzle	o	overcast	s	snow
f	fog	p	passing shower	tl	thunderstorm

Slight intensity is indicated by a small suffix " $_0$ " added to the small Beaufort letter, great intensity by a capital letter instead of a small one, continuity by a repetition of the letter, and intermittence by prefixing the letter " i." When precipitation occurs within sight of, but not at, a station the letter " j " precedes the Beaufort letter. A combination of Beaufort letters indicates the simultaneous occurrence of two or more phenomena. A solidus " / " divides existing weather from conditions during the preceding hour.

Examples :— r_0 = slight rain, r = moderate rain, R = heavy rain.

ss = continuous moderate snow.

ir_0s_0 = intermittent slight sleet.

jprh = shower of rain and hail can be seen but is not overhead.

bcm = fair weather with mist.

c/d = weather is now cloudy, but drizzle occurred within the last hour.

Fronts, which are the lines on the weather map where the boundary surfaces between air masses of different origin and characteristics cut the surface of the ground, are indicated in the following ways :—

= warm front. The air moving towards this boundary is warm and is normally of tropical or sub-tropical origin while the air moving away from the boundary is cold being normally of polar, sub-polar or maritime-polar origin.

= cold front. Here the air moving towards the boundary is cold while the air moving away from the front is warm.

= occluded front. The sector of the depression containing the warm air and which is included between the warm and cold fronts is called the warm sector. When the cold front overtakes the warm front the warm sector is lifted off the ground and the front formed when the warm and cold fronts thus coalesce is called an occluded front.

The symbols are placed on that side of the frontal line towards which the front is moving.

† For further details reference should be made to the " Weather map "[5] and the " Meteorological glossary "[6].

GRAPHS OF AVERAGE HOURLY PRESSURE.—These graphs show the average pressure at each exact hour G.M.T. for the six alternate months—January, March, May, July, September and November— and finally for the year, at the four observatories Aberdeen, Eskdalemuir, Kew and Valentia. At Eskdalemuir the period covered was 1911-1930; at the other three, 1901-1930. All values have been reduced to gravity in latitude 45°, but not to mean sea level. The heights of the barometer cisterns were : Aberdeen 85·3 feet, Eskdalemuir 778·3 feet, Kew 34·1 feet, Valentia 44·9 feet. The pressure values were based on hourly tabulations of accurate photographic records of mercury barometers.

BIBLIOGRAPHY

[1] London, Meteorological Office. Meteorological observer's handbook. London, 1942.

[2] BUCHAN, A. ; The mean atmospheric pressure and temperature of the British Isles. *J. Scot. met. Soc., Edinburgh,* Third series, **11,** 1900, p. 3.

[3] London, Meteorological Office. *Dly Weath. Rep., London.*

[4] GARBETT, L. G. ; Admiral Sir Francis Beaufort and the Beaufort scales of wind and weather. *Quart. J.R. met. Soc., London,* **52,** 1926, p. 161.

[5] London, Meteorological Office. Weather map. London, 1939 (reprinted 1950).

[6] London, Meteorological Office. Meteorological glossary. London, 1939 (reprinted 1950).

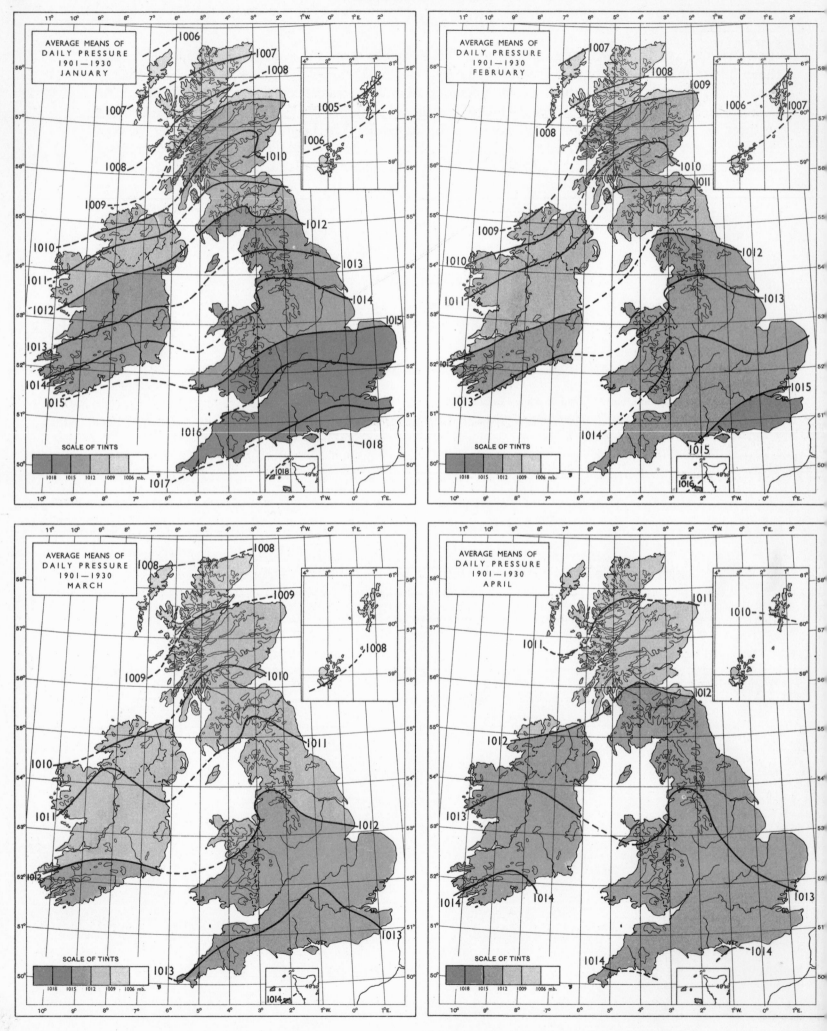

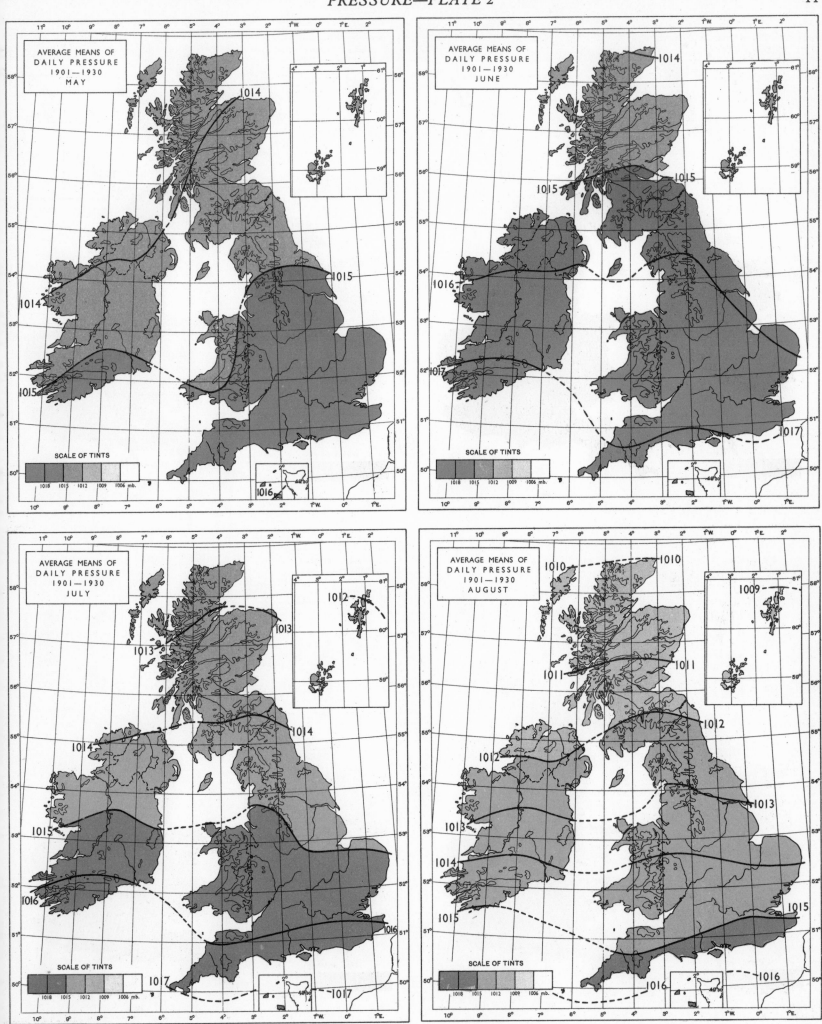

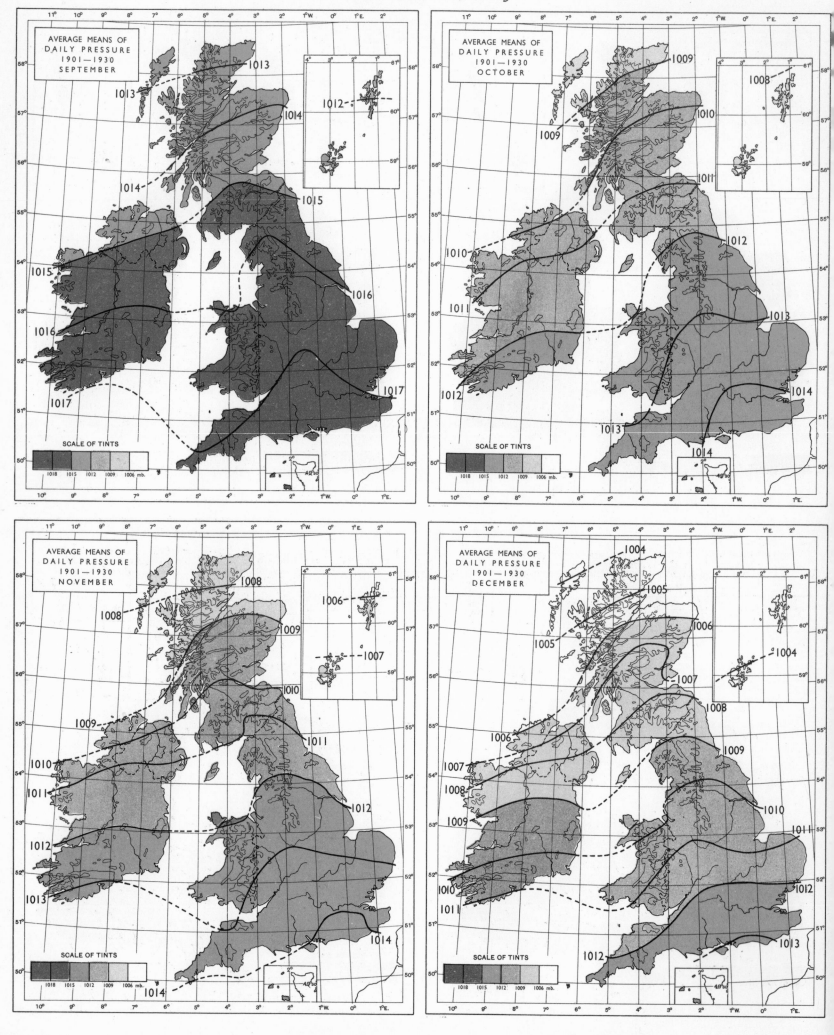

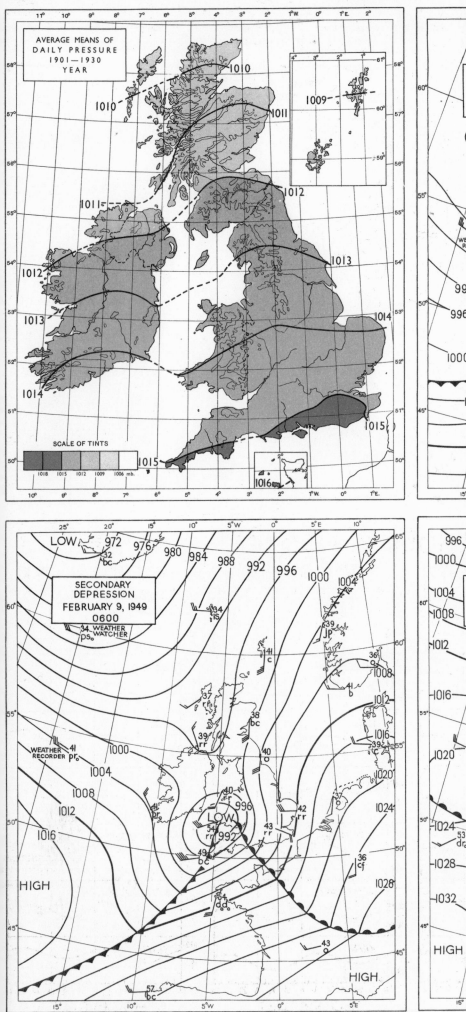

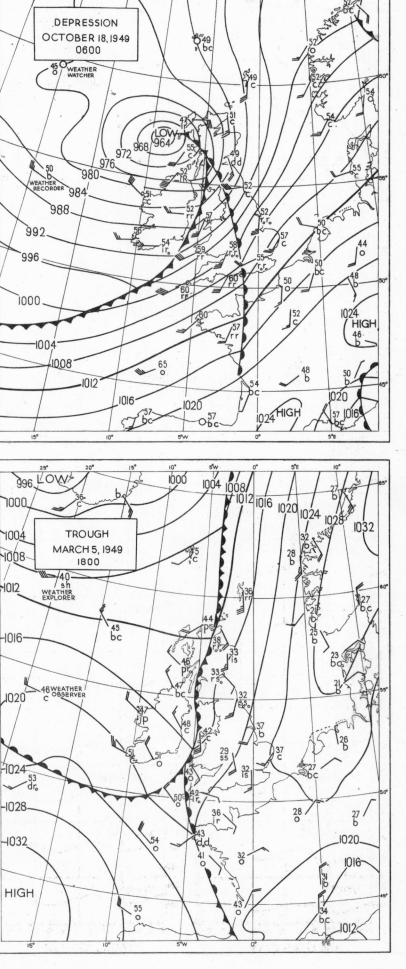

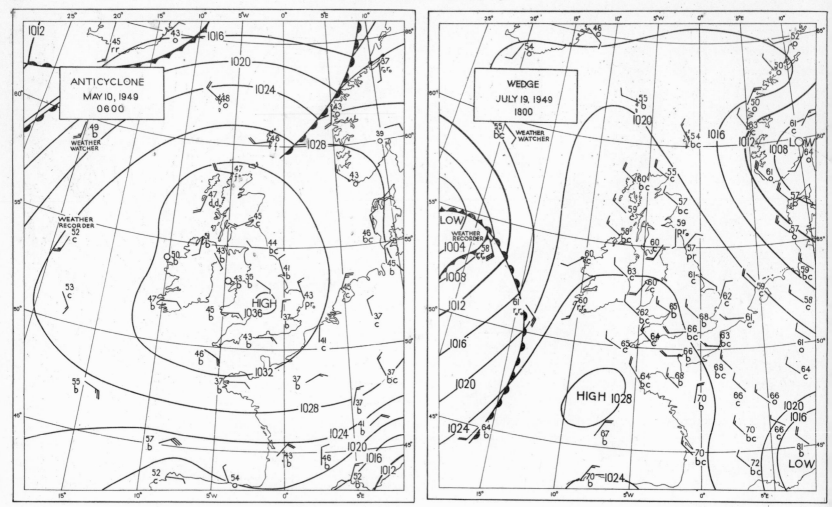

AVERAGE HOURLY PRESSURE

ABERDEEN 1901–1930   ESKDALEMUIR 1911–1930   KEW 1901–1930   VALENTIA 1901–1930

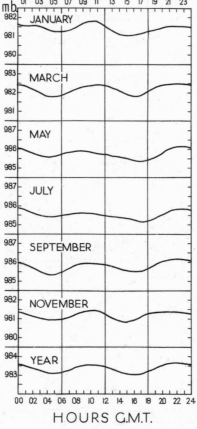
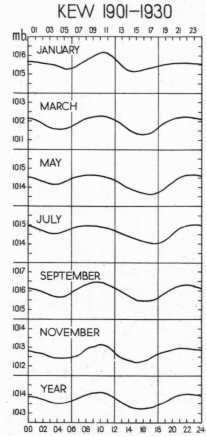
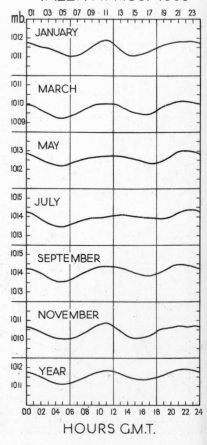

HOURS G.M.T.   HOURS G.M.T.   HOURS G.M.T.   HOURS G.M.T.

section, the " effective height " for each of them was determined, and then all the speed records were reduced to the standard height of 33 feet by means of Table II. This is based on a formula given by Hellmann[7] :—

$$V_h = V_{10} \ (0 \cdot 233 + 0 \cdot 656 \ \log \ (h + 4 \cdot 75))$$

where V_h is the speed at " effective height " h (in metres) and V_{10} is the speed at 10 metres.

TABLE II.—RATIO V_h/V_{10} FOR DIFFERENT VALUES OF h

Height in metres ...	2	3	4	5	10	15	20	25	30	35	40
Height in feet ...	7	10	13	16	33	49	65	82	98	115	131
Velocity Ratio V_h/V_{10}	0·78	0·82	0·85	0·89	1·00	1·08	1·15	1·20	1·24	1·28	1·32

Table III shows the speed of the highest gusts which have been recorded by anemographs in the British Isles. These values are quoted as read and are not reduced to standard height.

TABLE III.—GUSTS EXCEEDING 100 M.P.H., 1922-1947

	Height of vane of anemometer above ground	Highest gust	Date
	ft.	m.p.h.	
Bell Rock	131	101	October 19, 1935
Liverpool (Bidston)	64	101	January 29, 1938
Falmouth (Pendennis Castle)	65	103	March 8, 1922
Falmouth (Pendennis Castle)	65	103	December 6, 1929
Paisley	81	104	January 28, 1927
Holyhead	25	107	February 28, 1937
Tiree	50	108	January 28, 1927
Dunfanaghy Road (Ireland)	47	109	January 28, 1927
Scilly...	65	111	December 6, 1929
St. Ann's Head	70	>113	January 18, 1945

PLATE 1

MAP OF AVERAGE WIND SPEED, 1926-1940.—This map is based on hourly values obtained from pressure-tube anemograms, and represents the average wind speed at 33 feet above level, open country. It will be seen that the wind speed shows two tendencies : first, a general decrease from west to east, and second, a more rapid decrease from the coasts inland. The greatest average speed is found on the west coasts of Ireland and Scotland and the smallest near the centre of England.

MAP OF APPROXIMATE AVERAGE ANNUAL NUMBER OF DAYS WITH GALE, 1918-1937.— At stations with pressure-tube anemographs a day with gale is defined as one on which the mean line of the trace (*i.e.* the line half-way between the gusts and lulls) reaches or exceeds a speed of 39 m.p.h. even if only for a few minutes. At stations without anemographs a day of gale is one on which Beaufort force 8 or higher is observed for not less than ten minutes at any time of the 24 hours ending at midnight. Table I shows that force 8 is equivalent to a wind speed of 39-46 m.p.h. The map is based mainly on estimated Beaufort forces. The effect of nearness to the coast is shown very clearly, especially the high frequency of gales on the western seaboard.

DIAGRAM OF AVERAGE HOURLY VECTOR WIND AT MILDENHALL, 1938-1944.—The average hourly vector wind is the total displacement which would be experienced by a particle of air as a result of the winds during that hour on all days of the month in question over the period of observation, divided by the total number of hours. It is generally determined by resolving each hourly wind velocity into components from north and east (southerly and westerly winds having negative components), adding the values of each component algebraically, dividing by the number of hours, and combining the two average components.

Hourly values of wind speed and direction were measured from anemograms for the period of 60 minutes ending at each exact hour. In the diagram the average values are centred at the half-hours. The arrows fly with the wind and their lengths are proportional to the average hourly vector wind. The diurnal variation of wind shows a veer in the afternoon, which is small in January but is strongly marked in July.

MAP OF SPEED IN EXTREME GUSTS, 1923-1947.—During any one gust over open country it is not to be expected that the speed will change in any regular manner with height. On the average, however, the maximum gust does increase with height, although more slowly than in the case of mean speed. The gusts measured by the anemograph at a height of 150 feet at Cardington suggest that in gales the maximum gust at that height does not exceed the geostrophic wind, that is the wind at approximately 2,000 feet. It seems likely, therefore, that there is little variation in the gust speed above 150 feet.

The following formula, due to Bilham[8], connects gust speed with height above the ground :—

$$V_{G_h} = V_{G_{33}} \; (0 \cdot 588 + 0 \cdot 24 \log (h + 16)),$$

where V_{G_h} is the gust speed at height h in feet, and $V_{G_{33}}$ is the gust speed at the standard height of 33 feet. Values of the ratio $V_{G_h}/V_{G_{33}}$ computed from this formula are given in Table IV.

TABLE IV.—RATIO $V_{G_h}/V_{G_{33}}$ FOR DIFFERENT VALUES OF h

Height h (feet)... ...	33	40	50	65	80	97	130	162	330
$V_{G_h}/V_{G_{33}}$	1	1·015	1·032	1·060	1·072	1·090	1·120	1·130	1·210

The map has been prepared by extracting the values of extreme gust speeds recorded on anemograms and then correcting these values to standard height by means of Table IV, in order to make the values comparable. This process is exceptional : in making and publishing observations of maximum gust values it is the practice to record such values as read, and not to correct for the height of the vane.

PLATES 2-8

WIND ROSES SHOWING FREQUENCY OF FORCE AND DIRECTION OF THE WIND AT SELECTED STATIONS.—These diagrams are based on summaries of the percentage frequency of winds of different forces on the Beaufort wind scale. Only anemograph records have been used, the recorded speeds having been converted to Beaufort forces by means of Table I. Where the effective height of the anemograph differed from the standard of 33 feet, the speeds were first corrected by the ratios in Table II. The original summaries gave directions in sixteen compass points, N., NNE., NE., etc. ; these were reduced to eight points by sharing the winds for the intermediate points NNE., ENE., etc., between the two neighbouring directions. For example, if the percentage frequencies from N., NNE. and NE., were respectively N, P, Q, then P was divided between N. and NE. in the proportion $(P + N/3)/(P + Q/3)$.

The speeds of the winds have been classified, according to the Beaufort scale, into five categories, thus :—

Category	Beaufort force	Equivalent Speeds	
		m.p.h.	kt.
Light breeze	1-3	1-12	1-10
Moderate breeze	4	13-18	11-16
Fresh to strong wind	5-6	19-31	17-27
Moderate gale...	7	32-38	28-33
Gale, storm or hurricane	8-12	above 38	above 33

The plotted diagram is known as a " wind rose." The particular form adopted, combining force and direction, is a modification of one introduced by Nav.-Lieut. C. W. Baillie in 1892 and known as the Baillie wind rose. One inch along an arrow (which flies with the wind) represents a frequency of 25 per cent. ; from the head of the arrow to the circle is 5 per cent. The percentage frequency of calms (wind speed less than 1 m.p.h.) is shown by the figure within the circle. The thickness of an arrow indicates Beaufort forces 1-3, 4, 5-6, 7, and 8 and above. The periods covered by the observations and the effective heights of the anemographs are given on Plate 8.

BIBLIOGRAPHY

[1] ROBINSON, T. R. ; Description of an improved anemometer for registering the direction of the wind and the space which it traverses in given intervals of time. *Trans. R. Irish Acad., Dublin*, **22**, 1850, p. 155.

[2] BECKLEY, R. ; Description of the self-recording anemometer. *Rep. Brit. Ass., London*, 1858, p. 306.

[3] DINES, W. H. ; Anemometer comparisons. *Quart. J.R. met. Soc., London*, **18**, 1892, p. 165.

[4] GOLD, E. ; Wind in Britain. *Quart. J.R. met. Soc., London*, **62**, 1936, p. 167.

[5] London, Meteorological Office. Meteorological observer's handbook. London, 1942.

[6] GARBETT, L. G. ; Admiral Sir Francis Beaufort and the Beaufort scales of wind and weather. *Quart. J.R. met. Soc., London*, **52**, 1926, p. 161.

[7] HELLMANN, G. ; Über die Bewegung der Luft in den untersten Schichten der Atmosphëre. Zweite Mitteilung. *S.B. preuss. Akad. Wiss., Berlin*, 1917, No. 10, p. 174.

[8] BILHAM, E. G. ; Note on extreme gusts recorded in the British Isles. Building Research Board, Wind Pressure Committee Report, No. 734, 1938. Unpublished.

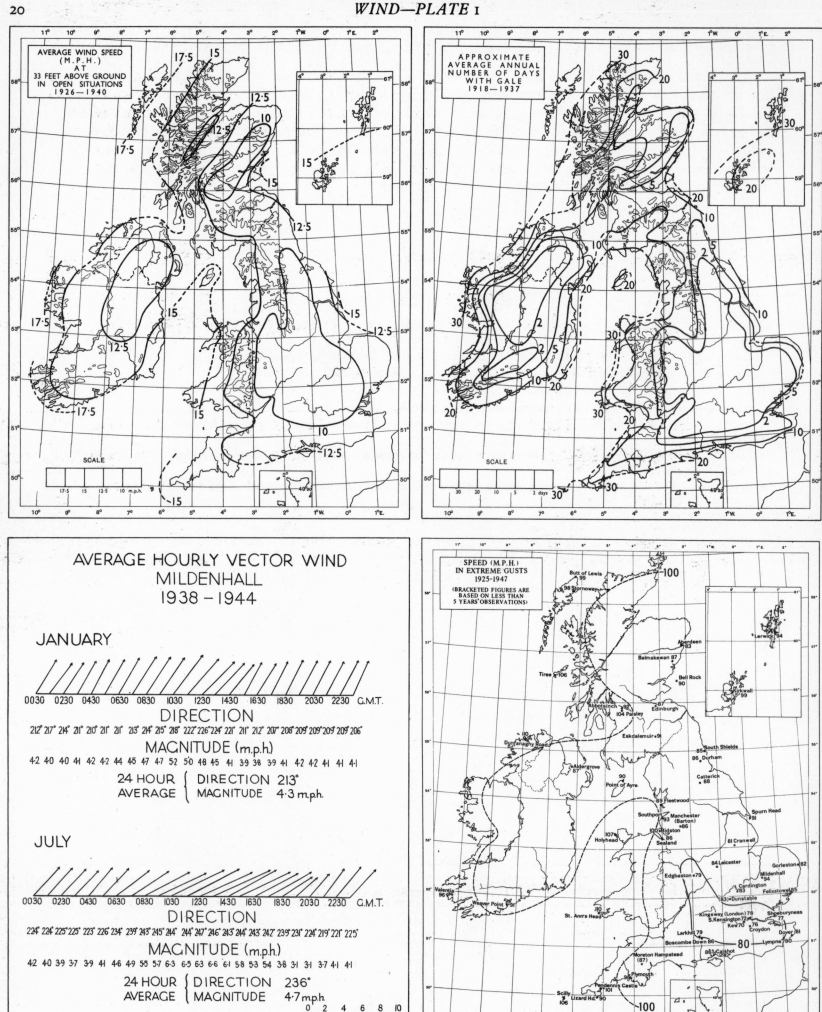

FREQUENCY, FORCE AND DIRECTION OF THE WIND AT SELECTED STATIONS

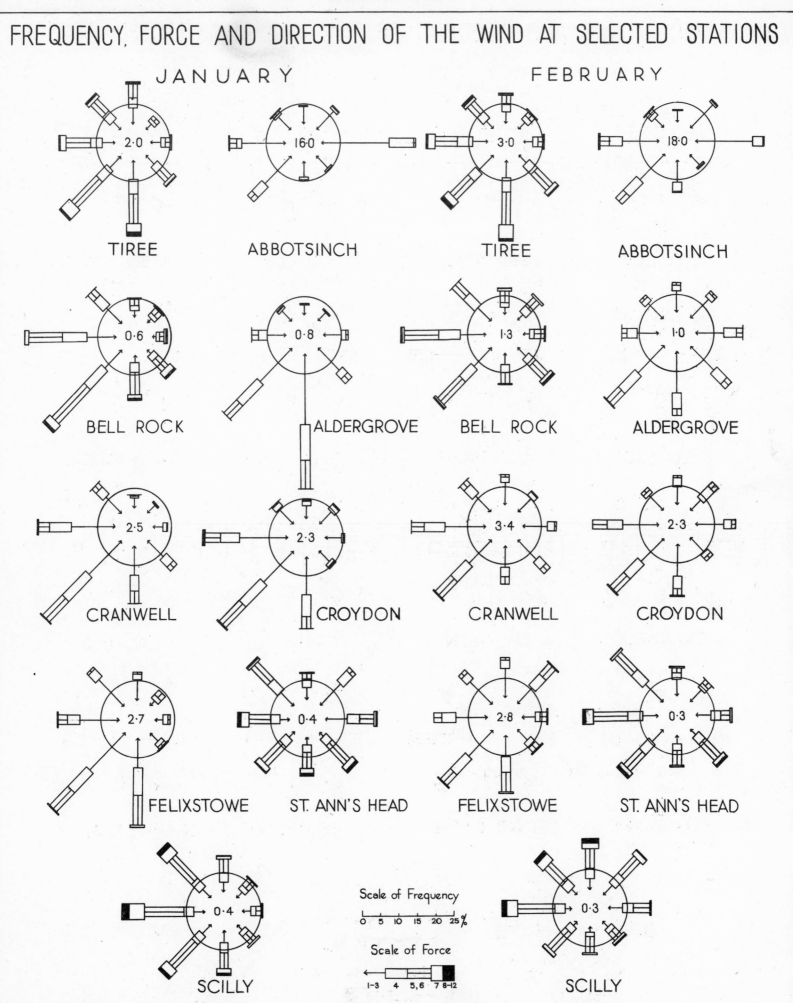

JANUARY

FEBRUARY

TIREE

ABBOTSINCH

TIREE

ABBOTSINCH

BELL ROCK

ALDERGROVE

BELL ROCK

ALDERGROVE

CRANWELL

CROYDON

CRANWELL

CROYDON

FELIXSTOWE

ST. ANN'S HEAD

FELIXSTOWE

ST. ANN'S HEAD

SCILLY

Scale of Frequency

0   5   10   15   20   25 %

Scale of Force

1-3   4   5,6   7 8-12

SCILLY

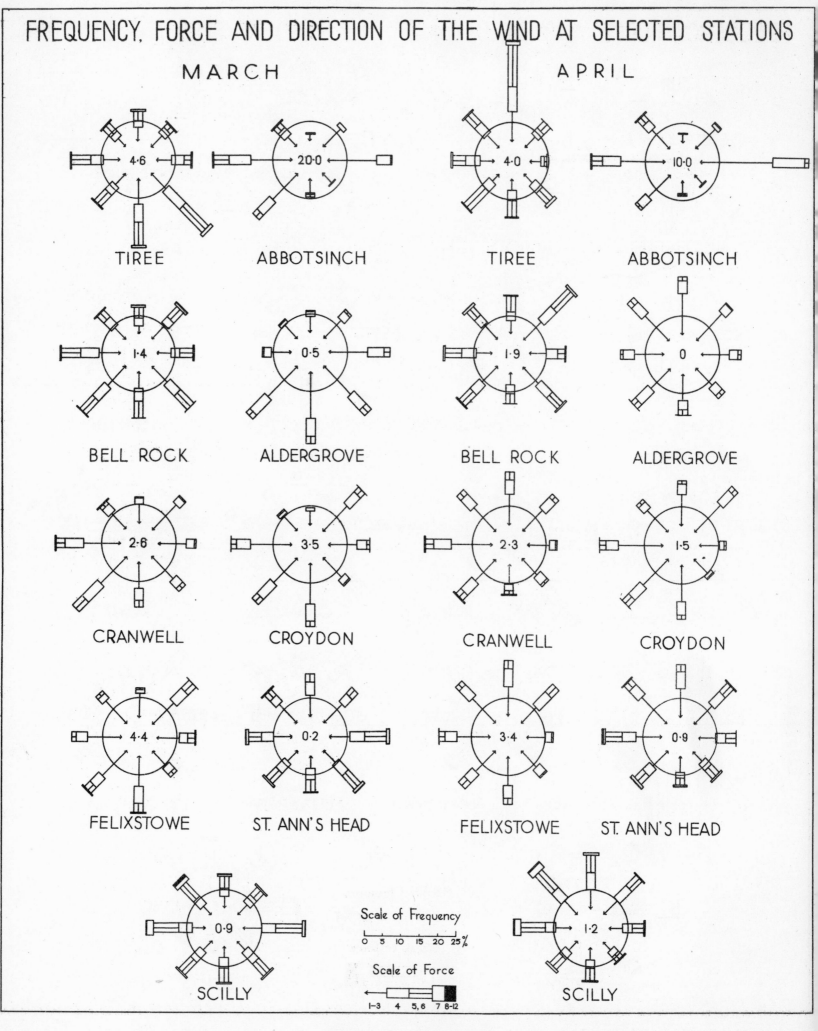

FREQUENCY, FORCE AND DIRECTION OF THE WIND AT SELECTED STATIONS

MARCH   APRIL

TIREE   ABBOTSINCH   TIREE   ABBOTSINCH

BELL ROCK   ALDERGROVE   BELL ROCK   ALDERGROVE

CRANWELL   CROYDON   CRANWELL   CROYDON

FELIXSTOWE   ST. ANN'S HEAD   FELIXSTOWE   ST. ANN'S HEAD

SCILLY   SCILLY

Scale of Frequency

0   5   10   15   20   25%

Scale of Force

1-3   4   5,6   7   8-12

FREQUENCY FORCE AND DIRECTION OF THE WIND AT SELECTED STATIONS

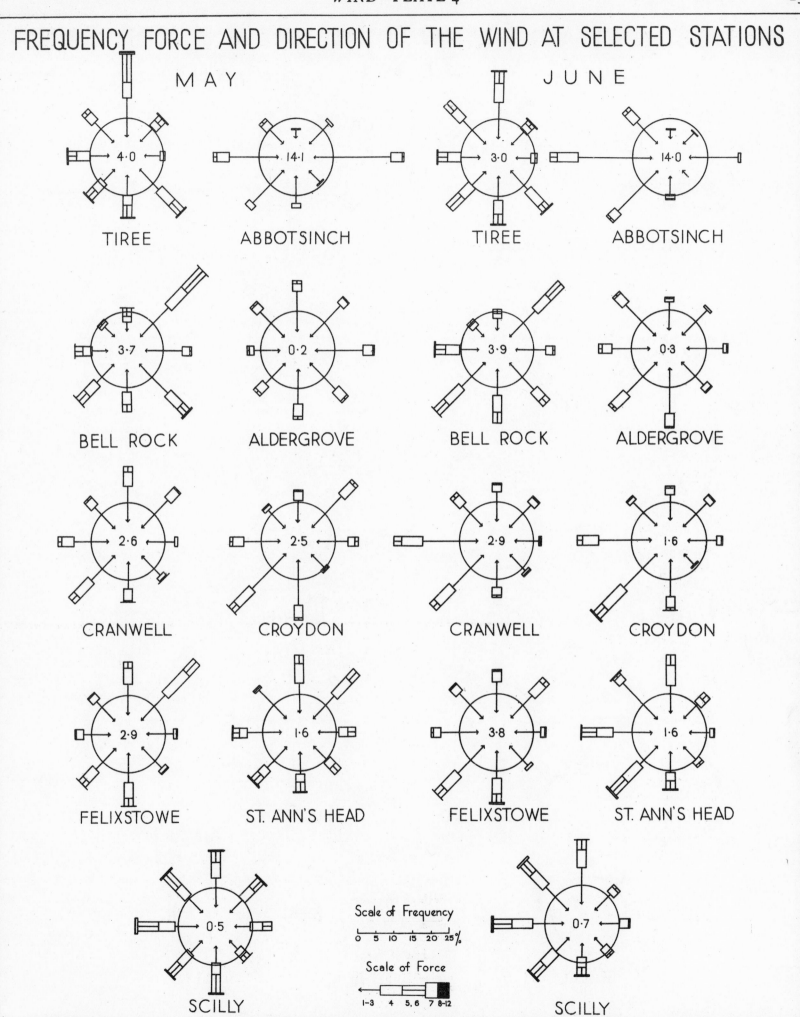

MAY

JUNE

TIREE   ABBOTSINCH   TIREE   ABBOTSINCH

BELL ROCK   ALDERGROVE   BELL ROCK   ALDERGROVE

CRANWELL   CROYDON   CRANWELL   CROYDON

FELIXSTOWE   ST. ANN'S HEAD   FELIXSTOWE   ST. ANN'S HEAD

SCILLY   SCILLY

Scale of Frequency

0 5 10 15 20 25%

Scale of Force

1-3   4   5, 6   7 8-12

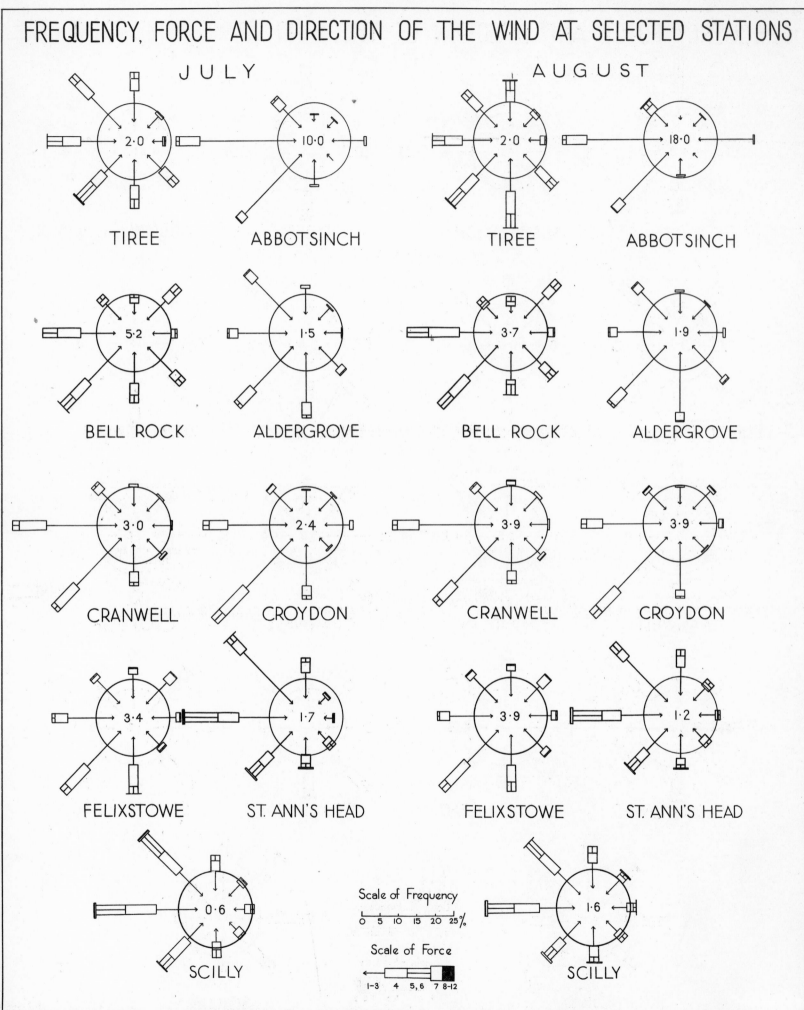

FREQUENCY, FORCE AND DIRECTION OF THE WIND AT SELECTED STATIONS

FREQUENCY, FORCE AND DIRECTION OF THE WIND AT SELECTED STATIONS

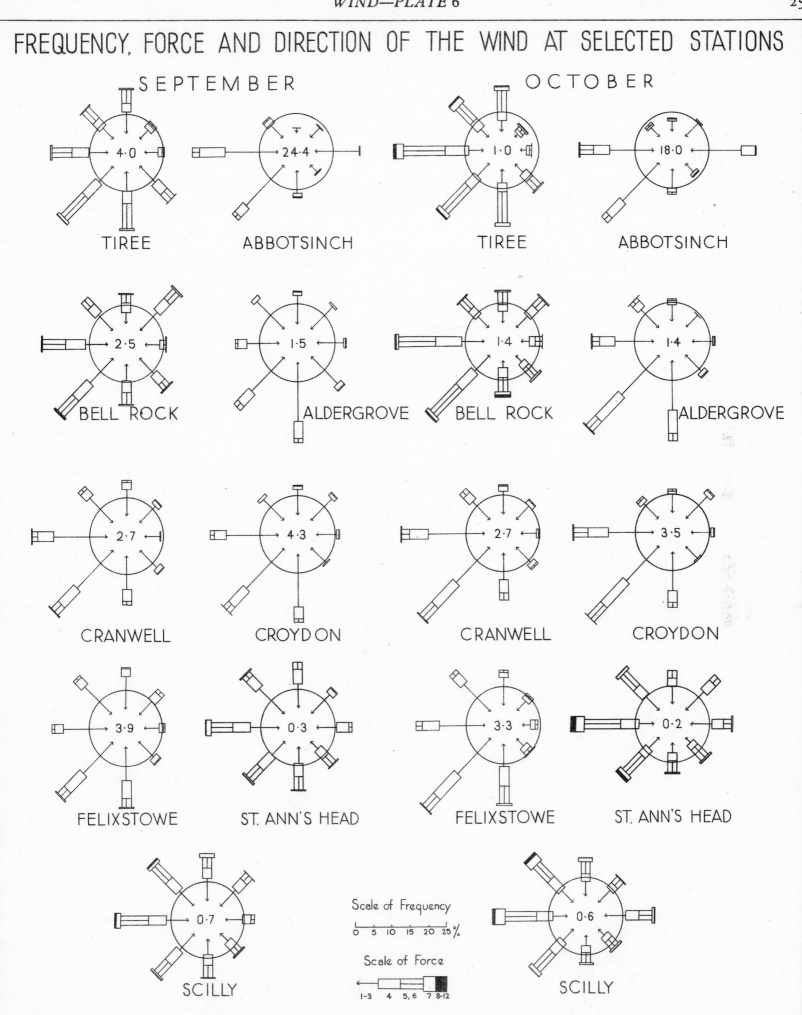

SEPTEMBER

OCTOBER

TIREE ABBOTSINCH TIREE ABBOTSINCH

BELL ROCK ALDERGROVE BELL ROCK ALDERGROVE

CRANWELL CROYDON CRANWELL CROYDON

FELIXSTOWE ST. ANN'S HEAD FELIXSTOWE ST. ANN'S HEAD

SCILLY SCILLY

Scale of Frequency

0 5 10 15 20 25 %

Scale of Force

1-3 4 5,6 7 8-12

FREQUENCY, FORCE AND DIRECTION OF THE WIND AT SELECTED STATIONS

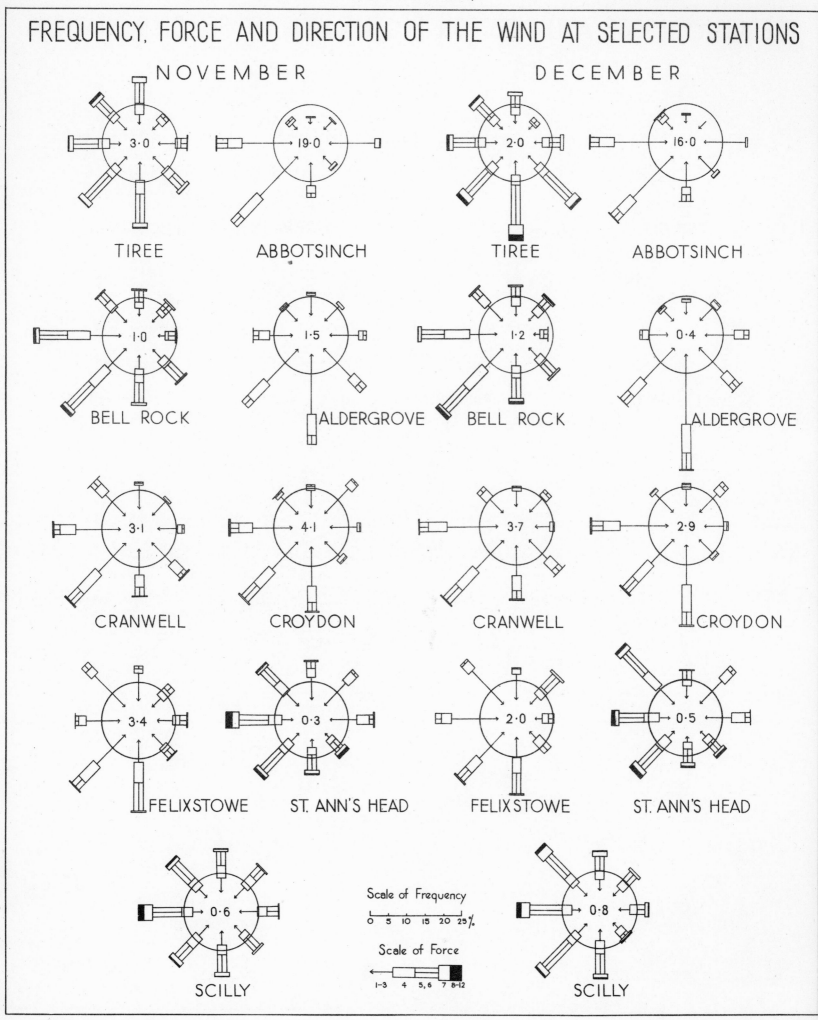

NOVEMBER

DECEMBER

TIREE

ABBOTSINCH

TIREE

ABBOTSINCH

BELL ROCK

ALDERGROVE

BELL ROCK

ALDERGROVE

CRANWELL

CROYDON

CRANWELL

CROYDON

FELIXSTOWE

ST. ANN'S HEAD

FELIXSTOWE

ST. ANN'S HEAD

SCILLY

Scale of Frequency

0 5 10 15 20 25 %

Scale of Force

1-3   4   5,6   7   8-12

SCILLY

FREQUENCY, FORCE AND DIRECTION OF THE WIND AT SELECTED STATIONS

YEAR

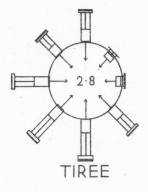

TIREE

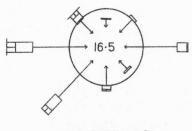

ABBOTSINCH

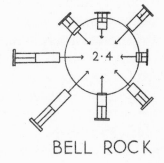

BELL ROCK

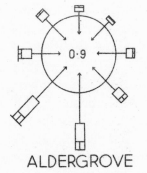

ALDERGROVE

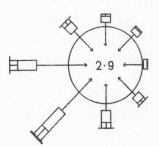

CRANWELL

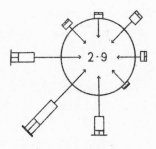

CROYDON

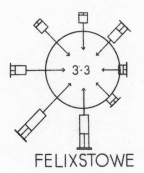

FELIXSTOWE

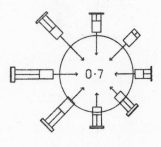

ST. ANN'S HEAD

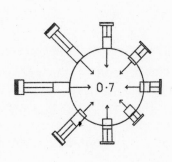

SCILLY

STATION	PERIODS COVERED BY OBSERVATIONS	EFFECTIVE HEIGHT
Tiree	1927–32 , 1934–36 , 1943	42 ft.
Abbotsinch	1938–42	34 ft. year and months corrected to 33 ft.
Bell Rock	1930–37 , 1939–40	about 23 ft.
Aldergrove	1927–38	33 ft.
Cranwell	1921–38	about 53 ft.
Croydon	1922–38	
Felixstowe	1925–36 , 1937–38	about 33 ft.
St Ann's Head	1935–43	year and months corrected to 33 ft.
Scilly	1922–27 , 1930–38	about 41 ft.

Scale of Frequency

0 5 10 15 20 25 %

Scale of Force

1–3 4 5,6 7 8–12

§3—TEMPERATURE

INTRODUCTION

The temperature maps are based on observations of *shade* or *screen* temperatures. The standard method of exposure of thermometers in the British Isles is in a Stevenson screen, which is a louvered box designed to allow the free passage of air through it without exposing the thermometers to radiation or contact with precipitation. The screen is erected on a level plot of short grass so that the thermometer bulbs are approximately four feet above the ground. Four thermometers are mounted in the screen, the dry-bulb, wet-bulb, maximum and minimum thermometers, and readings of all four are made at the time of the morning observation, usually 9h. The dry-bulb thermometer gives the air temperature at the time of observation, and, with the wet-bulb reading, the humidity. The former is also used to check the setting of the maximum and minimum thermometers. The minimum temperature usually occurs during the early hours of the morning, and the reading is credited in the records to the date of reading. The maximum temperature, on the other hand, is credited to the day previous to that of reading, as it usually occurs during the afternoon. On April 1, 1921, certain stations ceased to record such 24-hour extremes and recorded instead day maximum and night minimum readings. Details of these changes and a comparison of the results obtained by the two methods are set out in the Introduction to "Averages of temperatures for the British Isles,"[1]* but for all practical purposes the maps can be regarded as referring to 24-hour extremes. The arithmetical mean of the mean daily maximum and the mean daily minimum temperature during a month has been taken as giving the mean temperature for the month. This is a good approximation but on the average is 0·5 to 1°F. above the mean of 24-hourly readings[2].

The final values of the mean daily maximum, mean daily minimum and the mean temperatures have been corrected to mean sea level before being plotted on the maps. The normal decrease of temperature with height of 1°F. per 300 feet for the British Isles has been used throughout in making these corrections. They have been applied to eliminate variations due to altitude which would have made the maps as complicated as orographical ones. The *extremes* for individual days have not been corrected in this manner, but have been quoted as read.

HISTORICAL BACKGROUND

(a) Comparison of Temperatures over Two Long Periods

A comparison of the average monthly and annual temperatures for the British Isles for the years 1901-1930 with those for such other periods as have been published, has been produced by Glasspoole[3]. Values for 1901-1930 and 1871-1900, reduced to mean sea level, are given in Table I.

TABLE I.—COMPARISON OF AVERAGE MONTHLY AND ANNUAL TEMPERATURES

		Jan.	Feb.	Mar.	Apr.	May	June	July	Aug.	Sept.	Oct.	Nov.	Dec.	Year
							Degrees Fahrenheit							
1871-1900...	...	39·5	40·5	42·1	46·4	51·2	57·1	59·7	59·5	55·6	48·7	43·8	40·0	48·7
1901-1930...	...	40·7	40·7	42·6	45·9	51·8	56·2	59·6	59·0	55·5	50·0	43·6	41·2	48·9

The most noticeable feature is the milder winter half-year and cooler summer half-year during the more recent period.

(b) Warmest and Coldest Months on Record

The warmest and coldest months on record up to 1940 are given in Table II.

---

* The superior figures refer to the bibliography on page 32.

TABLE II.—WARMEST AND COLDEST MONTHS OVER THE BRITISH ISLES, 1881-1940

	Jan.	Feb.	Mar.	Apr.	May	June	July	Aug.	Sept.	Oct.	Nov.	Dec.	Year
Warmest	1916	1903	1938	1893	{1893 1919}	1940	1901	1899	1895	1921	1881	1934	1921
Coldest	1881	1895	1883	1917	1885	{1916 1927}	{1888 1922}	1912	1912	1892	1919	1890	1892

(c) Extremes of Temperature

The absolute extremes of temperature, with the place at which each was recorded, are given in Table III.

TABLE III.—EXTREMES OF TEMPERATURE ON RECORD FOR EACH MONTH

	Jan.	Feb.	Mar.	Apr.	May	June	July	Aug.	Sept.	Oct.	Nov.	Dec.
				Highest screen temperatures (°F.)								
Record	64	67	77	84	91	94	100·5	100	96	84	67	62
Day ...	23	28	29	20	24	16	22	9	2	6	8	10
Year ...	1828	1891	1929	1893	1922	1858	1868	1911	1906	1921	1847	1848
Place ...		Barnstaple		Cambridge		Greenwich		Greenwich		Greenwich		Greenwich
	London		Wakefield		Greenwich		Tonbridge		Bawtry		Greenwich	
				Lowest screen temperatures (°F.)								
Record	−16	−17	−3	5	14	23	26	27	18	11	−10	−16
Day ...	17	11	9	2	17	18	10	13	23	20	14	3
Year ...	1881	1895	1917	1917	1891	1903	1888	1887	1893	1880	1919	1879
Place ...		Braemar		Newton Rigg		Ben Nevis		Ben Nevis		Braemar		Kelso
	Kelso		Braemar		Ben Nevis		Ben Nevis		Ben Nevis		Braemar	

The temperature of −23°F. at Blackadder on December 4, 1879, often quoted as the lowest minimum for the British Isles, is not accepted because the exposure of the thermometer concerned was not standard.

It will be seen from Table III that the range of temperature recorded in each month was about 80°F., from 73°F. in both August and October to 84°F. in February. The absolute range of temperature recorded was 117·5°F. (100·5°F. at Tonbridge to −17°F. at Braemar).

Other extreme temperatures are given below :—

°F.					°F.			
98.9	Greenwich	...	August 19, 1932		−13	Aviemore	...	February 8, 1895
98	Raunds	...	August 9, 1911		−12	Braemar	...	February 8, 1895
98	Canterbury	...	August 9, 1911		−11	Buxton	...	February 11, 1895
98	Epsom	...	August 9, 1911		−10	Rhayader	...	January 21, 1940

PLATES 1-13

MAPS OF AVERAGE MONTHLY AND ANNUAL MEANS OF DAILY MAXIMUM, DAILY MINIMUM, DAILY RANGE AND DAILY MEAN TEMPERATURE, 1901-1930, REDUCED TO MEAN SEA LEVEL.—The maps are based on data published in "Averages of temperature for the British Isles "[1]. The average daily maximum temperature for any month is the mean of the daily maximum temperatures throughout this month averaged over the period 1901-1930. The average annual daily maximum temperature is the mean of the daily maximum temperatures throughout a year averaged over the 30 years. Similar definitions hold for the average daily minimum temperature. The average daily range is the difference between the average daily maximum and minimum temperatures, and the average daily mean temperature is half the sum of the average daily maximum and minimum temperatures over the 30 years. The isotherms have been drawn at intervals of 1°F. The maps show that in winter the run of the isotherms is mainly from north to south, so that temperature is lower in the east than in the west. In summer the isotherms run mainly from west to east, so that the north is cooler than the south.   Highest temperatures in the summer and lowest temperatures in the winter are recorded inland. The average daily range at all seasons is largest inland, the temperature being more uniform along the coasts.

It will be seen that July ranked as the warmest month nearly everywhere, but August had this distinction at most coastal stations in the south and also at many as far north as Rhyl and Scarborough and also to the north of Wick.   The coldest month was January over more than half of the British Isles, but it was February in coastal districts, over most of Wales, the English Lake District and south-west England.

PLATE 14

MAPS OF AVERAGE ANNUAL MAXIMUM AND MINIMUM TEMPERATURES, 1901-1930, AND OF ABSOLUTE MAXIMUM AND MINIMUM TEMPERATURES, 1901-1940.—In the preparation of the map of the average annual maximum temperature the average has been taken of the series of the one highest temperature each year during the period 1901-1930 for the stations included in "Averages of temperature for the British Isles"[1].   The map of average minimum temperature has been prepared in a similar manner.

The lower two maps are based on the absolute extremes recorded at the individual stations during the period 1901-1940.   It will be seen that there is a close similarity between the distributions of average maximum and absolute maximum temperatures and between the distributions of average minimum and absolute minimum temperatures.   The months which contributed the highest temperatures over the largest areas were August 1911, September 1906, and July 1934, the lowest temperatures having been mainly contributed by January 1940, January 1910, and January 1918.

Outstandingly warm days in the period were August 9, 1911 and August 19, 1932.   On the outstandingly cold day, January 21, 1940 (when $-10°F$. was recorded at Rhayader), the whole of the British Isles experienced a screen temperature below freezing point ($32°F$.) and more than half the area a temperature below $20°F$.

Plate 14 can be used to obtain the lowest temperature likely to be reached, at any particular place, on the average once in n years.   The rule is :—subtract from the normal annual minimum temperature x times the difference between the normal annual minimum and the absolute minimum for 40 years as read from the two maps for the place concerned, obtaining x from Table IV.

TABLE IV

Values of n	2	3	5	10	20
Values of x	0·00	0·22	0·43	0·65	0·84

PLATE 15

MAP OF RANGE OF AVERAGE MONTHLY TEMPERATURES, 1901-1930.—This map has been prepared from the station averages published in "Averages of temperature for the British Isles"[1], by plotting for each station the difference between the average temperatures of the warmest and coldest months.   The distribution on the map is distinct from that of the average daily range (Plate 13), where the values mainly increase from the coast inland.   In the case of the annual range of monthly mean temperatures the main increase in the values is from west to east.

MAPS OF AVERAGE DATES OF FIRST AND LAST SCREEN FROSTS, 1911-1940.—In the preparation of these maps use has been made of shorter records.   For such records estimates of the probable average dates for 1911-1940 have been made on the basis of the mean difference between the dates at these stations and at adjacent stations for which full records were available.   The records show that there is little correlation between the average date and the height of the station above mean sea level, *i.e.* the lower average temperature of hill stations is offset by the greater nocturnal fall of temperature in the valleys. There is, however, a rapid change of date from the coast inland and a marked change from the plains towards the centres of mountain masses. A few stations gave an average date much at variance with the dates for surrounding stations. These anomalous dates were due to a tendency for abnormally low minima, generally caused by local sheltering from the wind. Thus, in a hollow, with hills or woods beginning, say, 40 yards from the instrument enclosure, temperatures recorded on clear nights are lower than those in the surrounding countryside. At such places, even so far south as Rickmansworth, frosts may occur in July[4]. It has not been possible to indicate this local effect on the maps.

Town records may be affected by the local warmth of large built-up areas ; the area across the northern Midlands and around Birmingham, with the average date of the last spring frost before May 1, probably defines the conditions in towns rather than in the rural districts. If the stations had been confined to those in rural districts the proportion of the country with dates after May 1 and before November 1 would have been larger. In some very mild coastal districts the average dates were generally earlier than the middle of March and later than December 1 and in a few years there was complete absence of frost. These years have been omitted in computing the average but the resulting discrepancy is only appreciable over very small areas.

PLATE 16

MAPS OF AVERAGE ANNUAL FREQUENCY OF DAYS WITH MAXIMUM AND MINIMUM TEMPERA-
TURES WITHIN SPECIFIED LIMITS, 1913-1940.—These four maps show the average number of days a year with (a) maximum temperatures 32°F. or less ; (b) maximum temperatures 78°F. or more ; (c) minimum temperatures 32°F. or less ; and (d) minimum temperatures 60°F. or more. The maps are based on data given in the Annual Summary of the *Monthly weather report*, Table IX. The mean frequencies for 23 stations have been used, of which 11 were complete for the 28 years, 1913-1940. In drawing these maps, consideration has been given to the general distribution of the mountainous areas, but it has not been possible to define local variations. Thus, while the average number of days with a minimum temperature of 32°F. or less was 248 on the summit of Ben Nevis, it was only 62 at Fort William. The seasonal distribution of the number of days with a screen minimum temperature of 32°F. or less has been discussed by Lewis[5].

PLATE 17

GRAPHS OF AVERAGE ANNUAL VARIATION OF MONTHLY MAXIMUM, MINIMUM AND MEAN
TEMPERATURES, 1901-1930, AND OF THE FREQUENCY OF MAXIMUM AND MINIMUM TEM-
PERATURES.—In the left-hand diagram, the average monthly maximum, minimum and mean tempera-
tures, given in "Averages of temperature for the British Isles "[1], have been plotted for four representative stations—Deerness, Manchester, Kew and Valentia. In addition the diagrams show for each station the extreme maximum and extreme minimum temperature recorded each month during the period 1901-1940. The day and year of these monthly extremes are also indicated. A curve is also included of the average daily mean temperatures for Kew for the period 1871-1940. This curve is very irregular, although in its general trend it is similar to the smoother curve based on monthly values. Subsidiary maxima and minima occur at irregular intervals. Such relative warm and cold periods at Scottish stations have been discussed by Buchan[6]. Subsequent work[7] has shown that, while there may be a tendency for certain periods to be abnormally warm or cold for the season, these periods reveal wide fluctuations in incidence and intensity. Most of the minor irregularities of day-to-day average temperatures are probably the result of chance variations, and would not reappear in a different 70-year interval. The subject has also been discussed by Hawke[8].

The diagrams on the right-hand side give the average annual frequency of daily maximum and minimum screen temperatures at Deerness, 1913-1930 and at Kew, 1913-1940. The horizontal lines show the observed frequencies in steps of 9°F. using scale A to give the number of days. Thus the average number of days a year at Kew with maximum temperatures between 32·5°F. and 41·5°F. was 32. The smooth curve gives the calculated frequencies. For any given temperature on the horizontal scale the average number of days a year on which the maximum (or minimum) temperature will be within 2°F. on either side of that temperature is shown on the appropriate curve against scale B. Thus the curve shows that a maximum temperature of 40° ± 2°F. (38° to 42°F.) occurs at Kew on approximately 20 days during the year.

The diagram for Rothamsted shows the frequency per mille of maximum and minimum temperatures by degree steps for winter (December to February) and summer (July and August) during the 50 years 1878-1927. Any point on each curve therefore represents the probability that the temperature will be within 0·5°F. on either side of the value shown at the foot. It should be noted that the plotted points come nearly midway between the ordinates representing exact degrees. The reason for this is that the readings have been tabulated in degree steps, *e.g.* 50·0° to 50·9°F., and plotted against the mid values, in this case 50·45°F. June has been omitted because the means for this month were appreciably lower than those for July and August. The data for 1878-1926 were obtained from Fisher and Hoblyn[9]; those for 1927 have been added from figures supplied by the Director of the Rothamsted Experimental Station.

PLATE 18

GRAPHS OF DIURNAL VARIATION OF TEMPERATURE AT KEW FOR TWO HOT AND TWO COLD DAYS.—These graphs relate to the temperature at Kew for two hot days, August 9, 1911 and August 3, 1933, and for two cold days, February 14, 1929 and February 26, 1929. On August 9, 1911, the diurnal range was 31·7°F. (from 62·2°F. to 93·9°F.), on August 3, 1933, 13·1°F. (from 66·2°F. to 79·3°F.), on February 14, 1929, 14·4°F. (from 12·6°F. to 27·0°F.) and on February 26, 1929, only 1·5°F. (from 29·8°F. to 31·3°F.). On February 14, 1929, there were over two-and-a-half hours of bright sunshine, while on February 26, 1929, the day was continuously overcast.

GRAPH OF VARIATION OF TEMPERATURE, HUMIDITY AND WIND AT FELIXSTOWE DURING ONSET OF SEA BREEZE.—The graph of the variations of temperature at Felixstowe on May 1, 1942, shows the effect of a sea breeze and the accompanying changes in the humidity, wind force and direction. The temperature, which had risen to 51·2°F. about midday, fell 3°F. in 10 minutes and subsequently more slowly a further 2°F. Simultaneously the relative humidity increased by 20 per cent. and in all by about 33 per cent. (from 46 to 79 per cent.).

GRAPHS OF AVERAGE HOURLY TEMPERATURES, 1901-1930, FOR FOUR STATIONS.—This diagram shows the average hourly temperature and so also the diurnal variation of temperature at four observatories. The hourly values were recorded photographically. They have been published in the *Observatories' year book*. At Kew the averages of the hourly values are for the years 1901-1930 and at Eskdalemuir, 1911-1930. At Aberdeen and Valentia the averages are also for 1901-1930, but at these stations they have been obtained by adjusting those for the period 1871-1900 by the ratio of the diurnal ranges for 1901-1930 to those of 1871-1900. Graphs are given for alternate months and for the year, the broken portions of the curves being for the night period between sunset and sunrise. The diurnal range is smallest on the coast and also in the winter, and greatest inland and in summer. The temperature varies most rapidly just after sunrise and a little before sunset.

BIBLIOGRAPHY

[1] London, Meteorological Office. Averages of temperature for the British Isles for periods ending 1930, 1935. London, 1933, 1936.

[2] BROOKS, C. E. P.; True mean temperature. *Mon. Weath. Rev., Washington D.C.*, **49**, 1921, p. 226.

[3] GLASSPOOLE, J. ; Mean temperature over the British Isles. *Quart. J.R. met. Soc., London,* **67,** 1941, p. 47.

[4] HAWKE, E. L. ; Thermal characteristics of a Hertfordshire frost-hollow. *Quart. J.R. met. Soc., London,* **70,** 1944, p. 23.

[5] LEWIS, L. F. ; The seasonal distribution over the British Isles of the number of days with a screen minimum temperature of 32°F. or below. *Quart. J.R. met. Soc., London,* **69,** 1943, p. 155.

[6] BUCHAN, A. ; Interruptions in the regular rise and fall of temperature in the course of the year. *J. Scot. met. Soc., Edinburgh,* **2,** 1869, p. 4.

[7] BROOKS, C. E. P. and MIRRLEES, S. T. A. ; Irregularities in the annual variation of temperature of London. *Quart. J.R. met. Soc., London,* **56,** 1930, p. 375.

[8] HAWKE, E. L. ; Buchan's days. London (Lovat Dickson, Ltd.), 1937.

[9] FISHER, R. A. and HOBLYN, T. N. ; Maximum and minimum correlation tables in comparative climatology. *Geogr. Ann., Stockholm,* **10,** 1928, p. 267.

BAYARD, F. C. and MARRIOTT, W. ; The frost of January and February 1895 over the British Isles. *Quart. J.R. met. Soc., London,* **21,** 1895, p. 141.

BAYARD, F. C. ; English climatology. *Quart. J.R. met. Soc., London,* **29,** 1903, p. 1.

BELASCO, J. E. ; The temperature characteristics of different classes of air over the British Isles in winter. *Quart. J.R. met. Soc. London,* **71,** 1945, p. 351.

BILHAM, E. G. ; Variations in the climate of York during the 60 years, 1871-1930, and comparison with Oxford. *Quart. J.R. met. Soc., London,* **59,** 1933, p. 137.

BILHAM, E. G. ; The sea-breeze as a climatic factor. *J. State Med., London,* **42,** 1934, p. 40.

BRYANT, W. W. ; Abnormal temperature, with special reference to the daily maximum air temperature at Greenwich. *Quart. J.R. met. Soc., London,* **44,** 1918, p. 23.

BUCHAN, A. ; The mean atmospheric pressure and temperature of the British Islands. *J. Scot. met. Soc., Edinburgh,* **11,** 1898, p. 3.

BUCHAN, A. ; The meteorology of Ben Nevis [Dec. 1883-1904]. *Trans. roy. Soc., Edinburgh,* **34,** 1890 ; **42,** 1902 ; **43,** 1905 ; **44,** 1910.

DRUMMOND, A. J. ; Cold winters at Kew Observatory, 1783-1942. *Quart. J.R. met. Soc., London,* **69,** 1943, p. 17.

DUNBAR, W. ; Abnormally high and low daily mean temperatures, Kilmarnock, 1902-1941. *Quart. J.R. met. Soc., London,* **68,** 1942, p. 287.

GLASSPOOLE, J. and HOGG, W. H. ; Serial monthly values of mean temperature over the British Isles, 1881-1940, and annual values, 1866-1940. *Quart. J.R. met. Soc., London,* **68,** 1942, p. 45.

EATON, H. S. ; The mean temperature of the air at Greenwich (from September, 1811 to June, 1856, inclusive). *Quart. J.R. met. Soc., London,* **14,** 1888, p. 15.

HARDING, C. ; The abnormal summer of 1911. *Quart. J.R. met. Soc., London,* **38,** 1912, p. 1.

HAWKE, E. L. ; Extreme diurnal ranges of air temperature in the British Isles. *Quart. J.R. met. Soc., London,* **59,** 1933, p. 261.

HAWKE, E. L. ; Diurnal temperature range of 50·9°F. *Met. Mag., London,* **.71,** 1936, p. 186.

HEYWOOD, G. S. P. ; Katabatic winds in a valley. *Quart. J.R. met. Soc., London,* **59,** 1933, p. 47.

LEWIS, L. F. ; Variations of temperature at Oxford, 1815-1934. *Prof. notes met. Off., London,* **5,** No. 77, 1937.

London, Meteorological Office. Temperature tables for the British Isles, 1871-1900. London, 1902.

London, Meteorological Office. The book of normals of meteorological elements for the British Isles for periods ending 1915. Section III, Maps of the normal distribution of temperature, rainfall and sunshine. London, 1920. Section IVa, The range of variation of temperature and rainfall. London, 1923.

MANLEY, G. ; The climate of the northern Pennines ; the coldest part of England. *Quart. J.R. met. Soc., London,* **62,** 1936, p. 103.

MANLEY, G. ; Meteorological observations on Dun Fell, a mountain station in northern England. *Quart. J.R. met. Soc., London,* **68,** 1942, p. 151.

MARRIOTT, W. ; On the frost of December 1879 over the British Isles. *Quart. J.R. met. Soc., London,* **6,** 1879-1880, p. 102.

MARRIOTT, W. ; The abnormal weather of the past summer [1906] and some of its effects. *Quart. J.R. met. Soc., London,* **33,** 1907, p. 5.

MARRIOTT, W. ; The cold spell at the end of December 1908. *Quart. J.R. met. Soc., London,* **35,** 1909, p. 81.

MOSSMAN, R. C. ; Some aspects of the cold period December 1916 to April 1917. *Quart. J.R. met. Soc., London,* **43,** 1917, p. 401.

PETERS, S. P. ; Sea breezes at Worthy Down, Winchester. *Prof. notes met. Off., London,* **6,** No. 86, 1938.

SCOTT, R. H. and GASTER, F. ; Means of the daily minimum, daily average and daily maximum temperatures as recorded at the stations included in the daily and weekly weather reports during the 25 years, 1871-1895. *Quart. J.R. met. Soc., London,* **23,** 1897, p. 275.

TINN, A. B. ; Local temperature variations in the Nottingham district. *Quart. J.R. met. Soc., London,* **64,** 1938, p. 391.

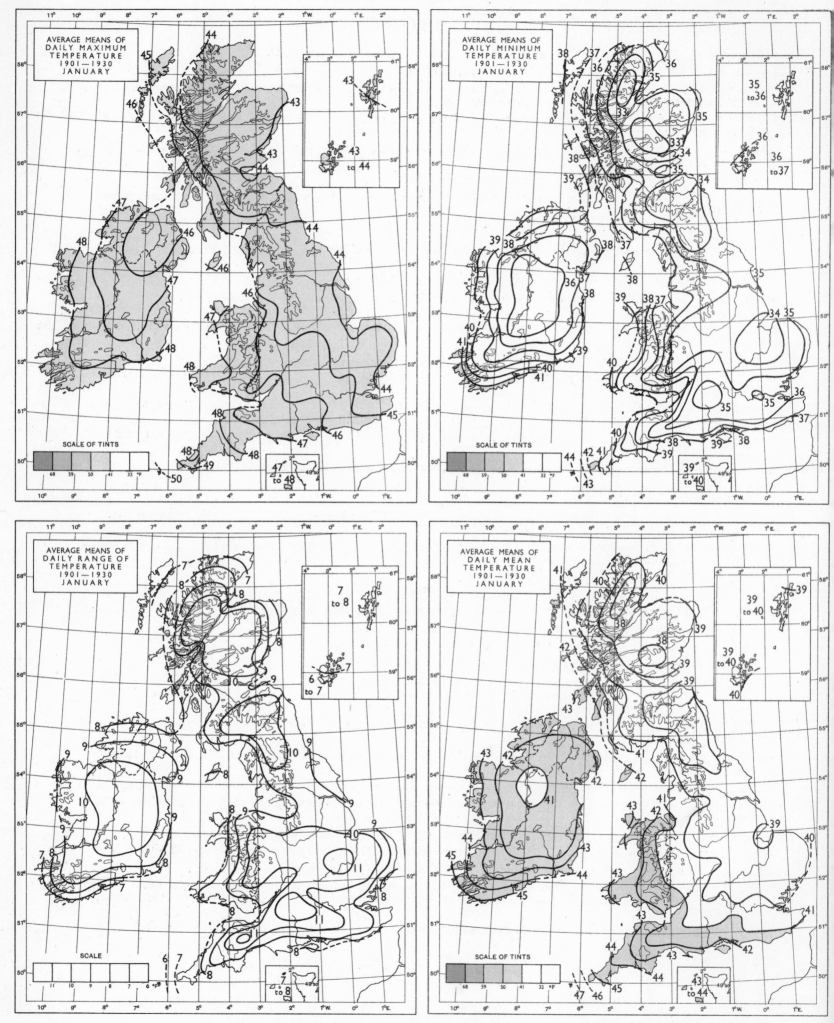

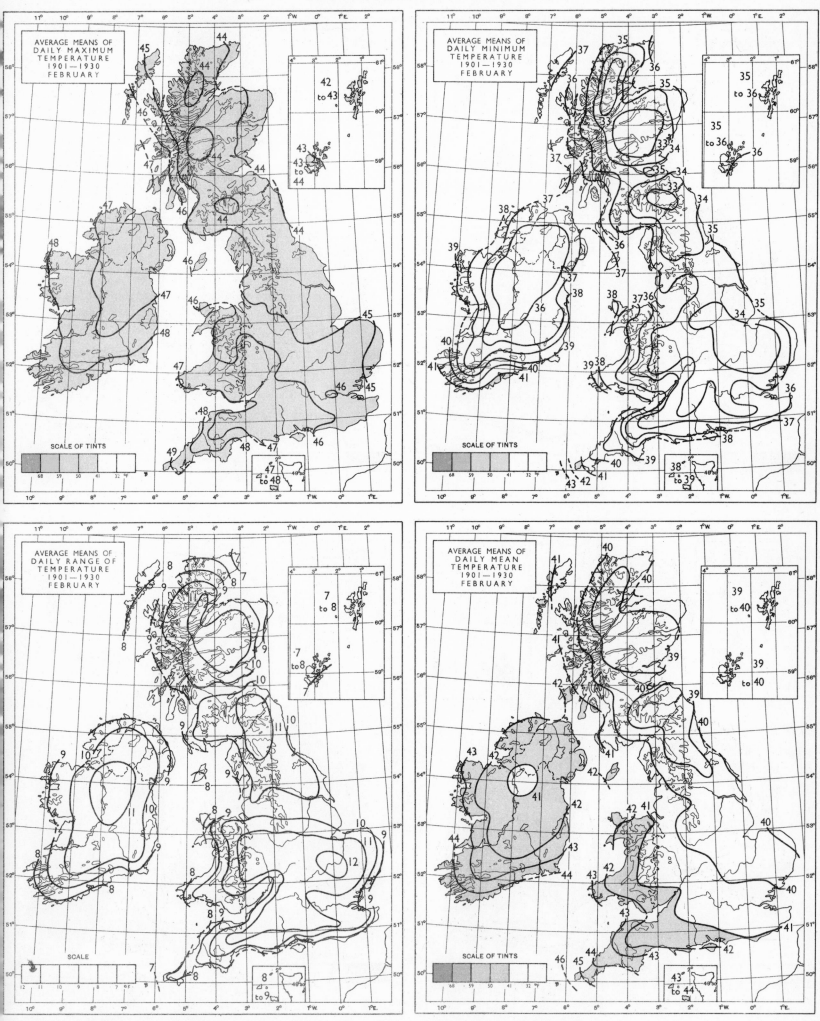

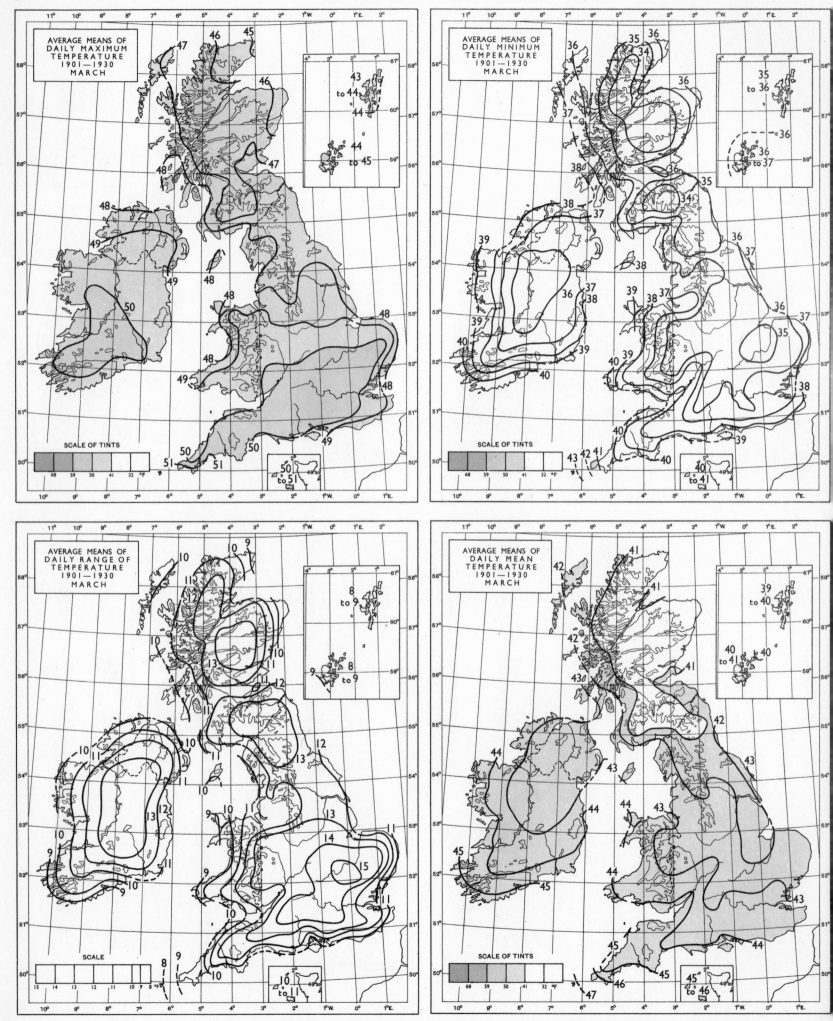

AVERAGE MEANS OF
DAILY MAXIMUM
TEMPERATURE
1901—1930
MARCH

SCALE OF TINTS

68   59   50   41   32 °F

AVERAGE MEANS OF
DAILY MINIMUM
TEMPERATURE
1901—1930
MARCH

SCALE OF TINTS

68   59   50   41   32 °F

AVERAGE MEANS OF
DAILY RANGE OF
TEMPERATURE
1901—1930
MARCH

SCALE

15 14 13 12 11 10 9 8

AVERAGE MEANS OF
DAILY MEAN
TEMPERATURE
1901—1930
MARCH

SCALE OF TINTS

68   59   50   41   32 °F

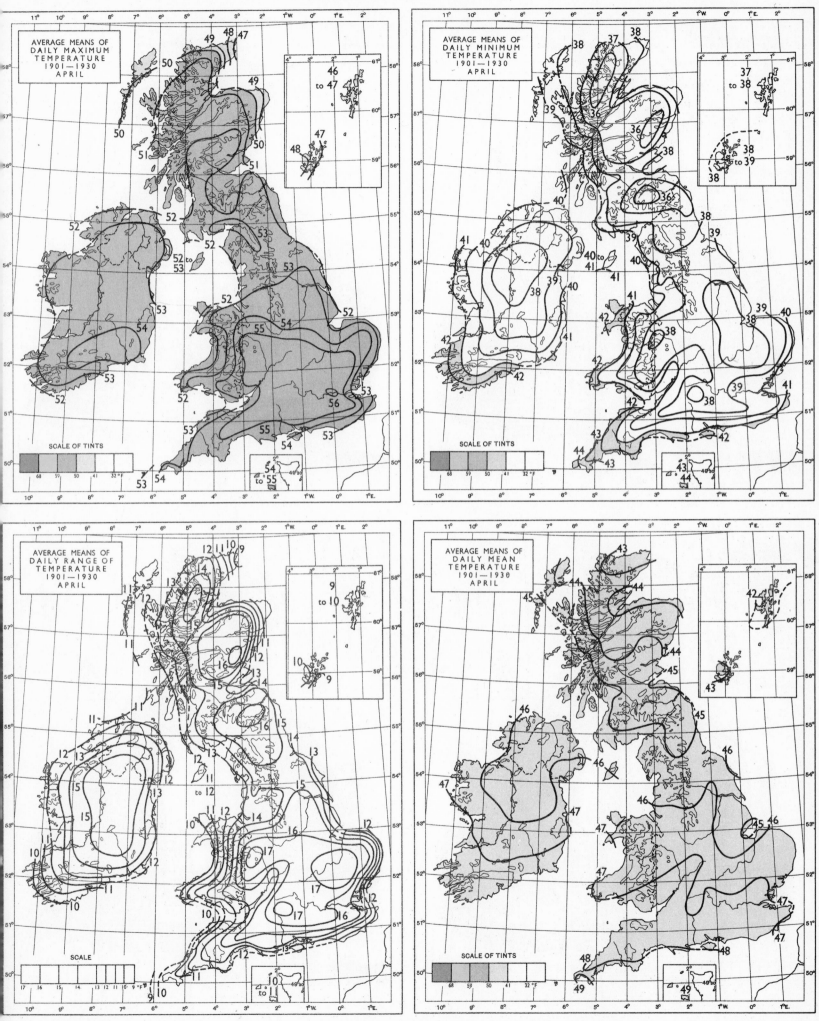

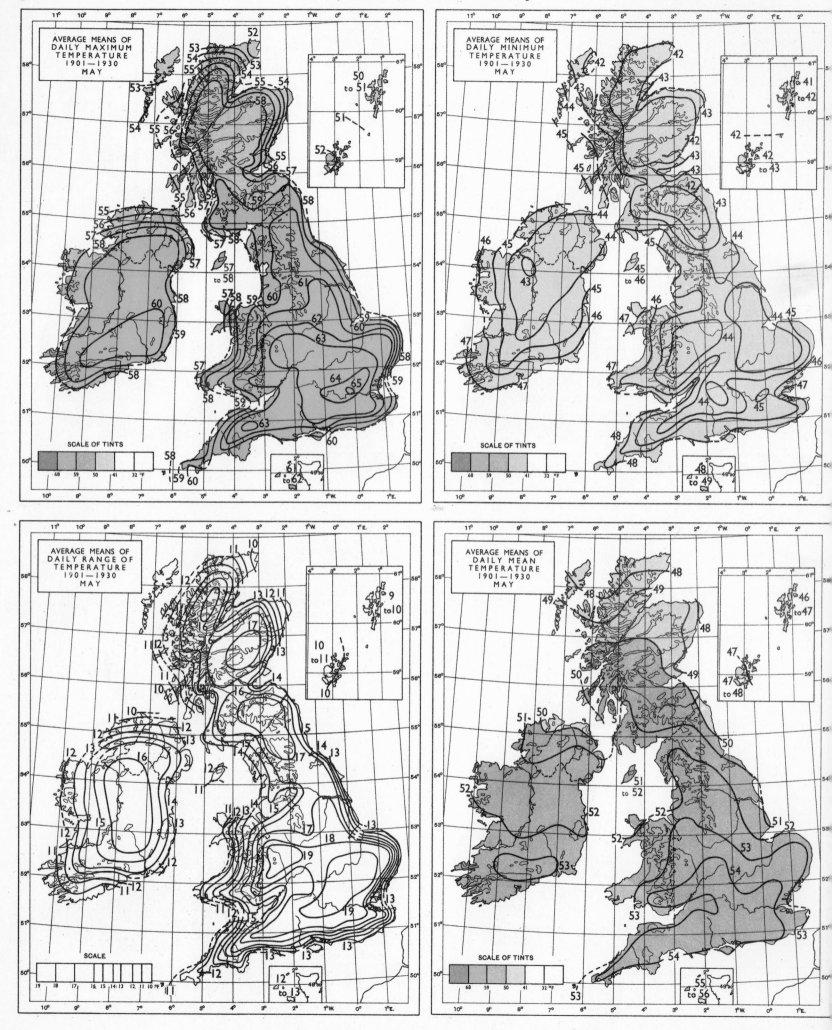

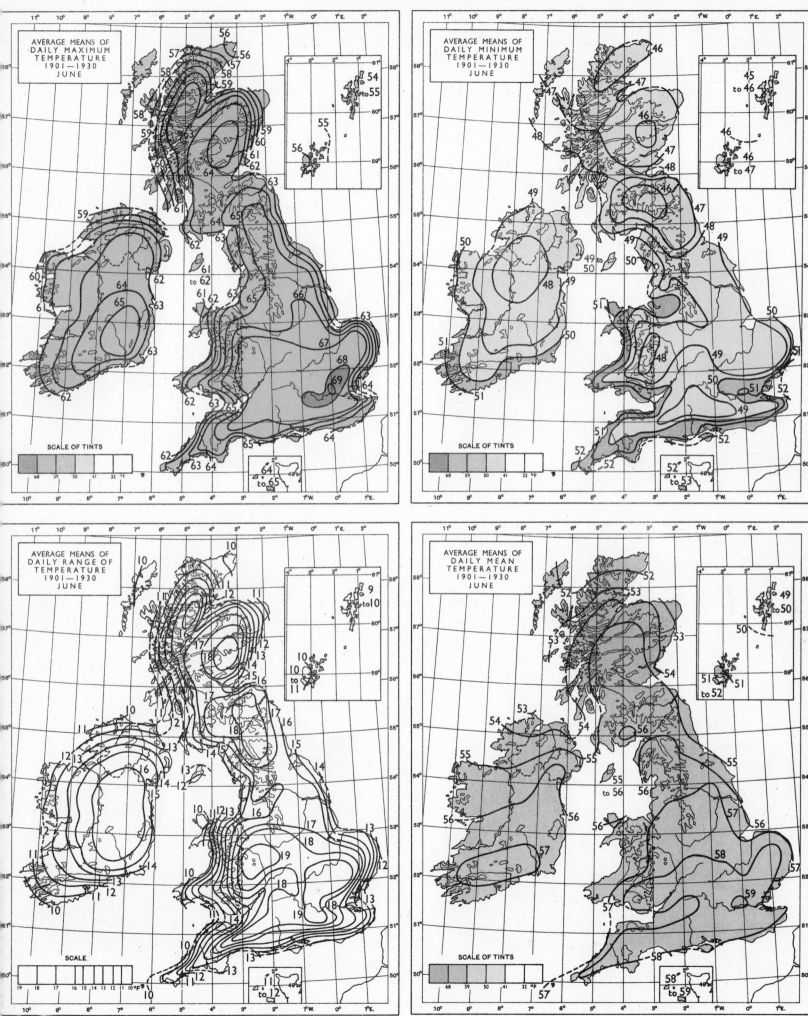

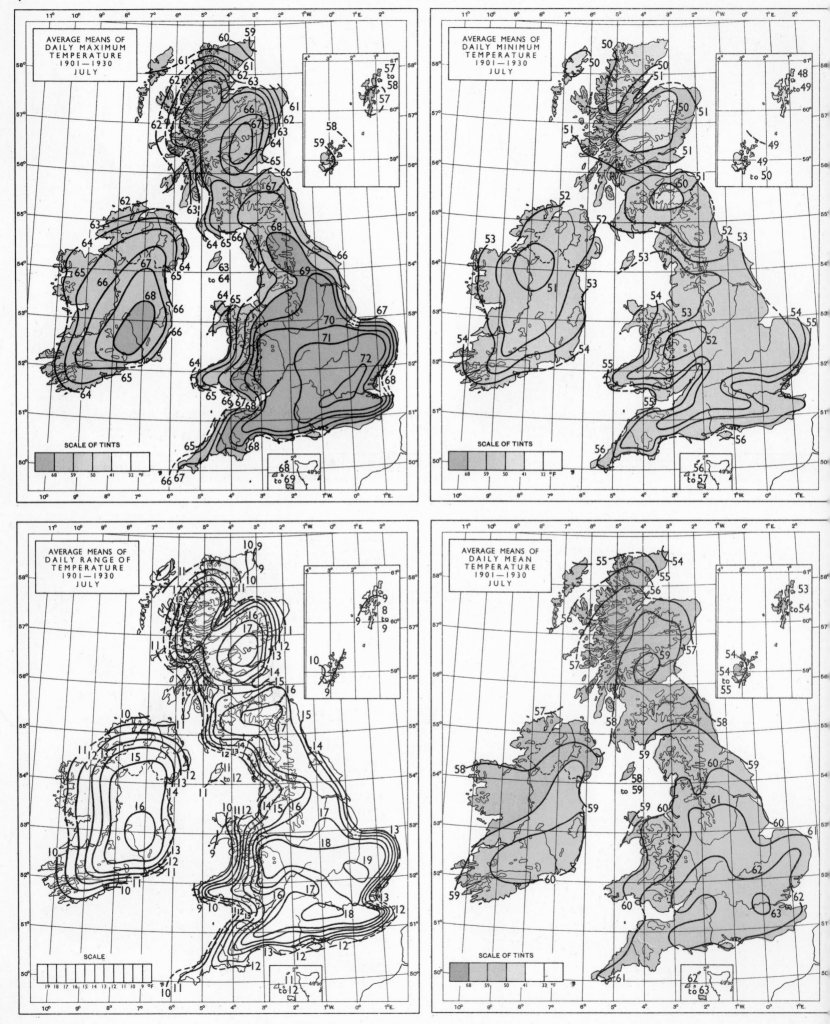

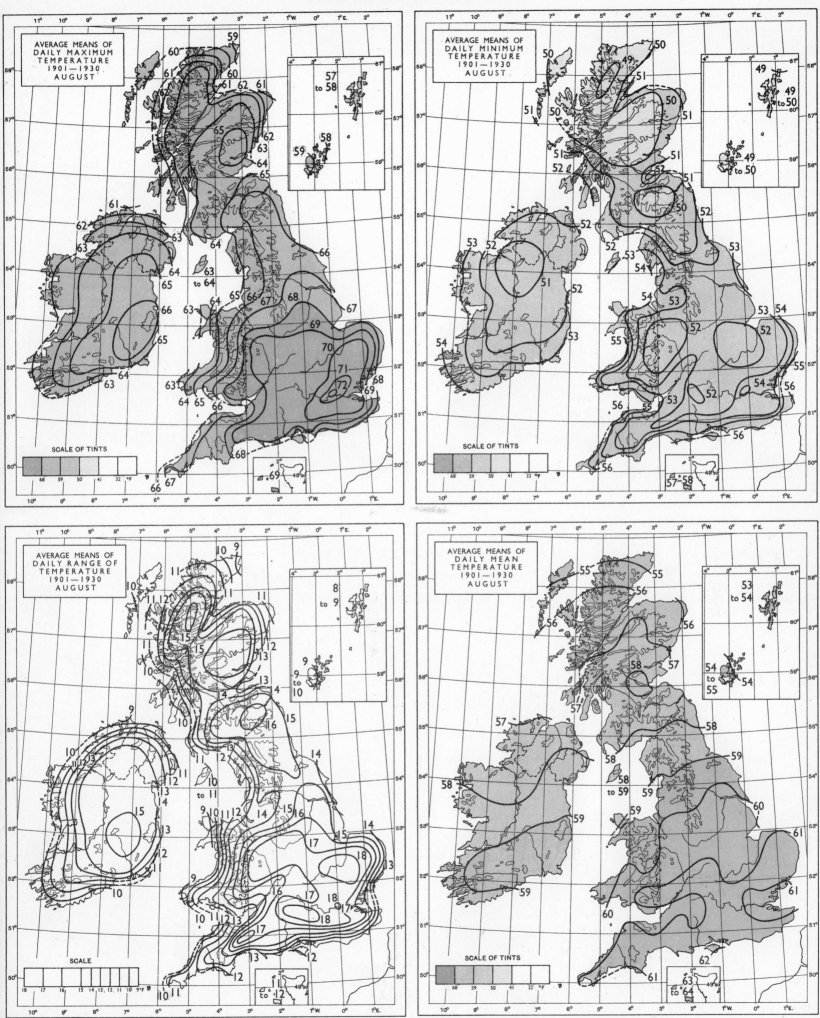

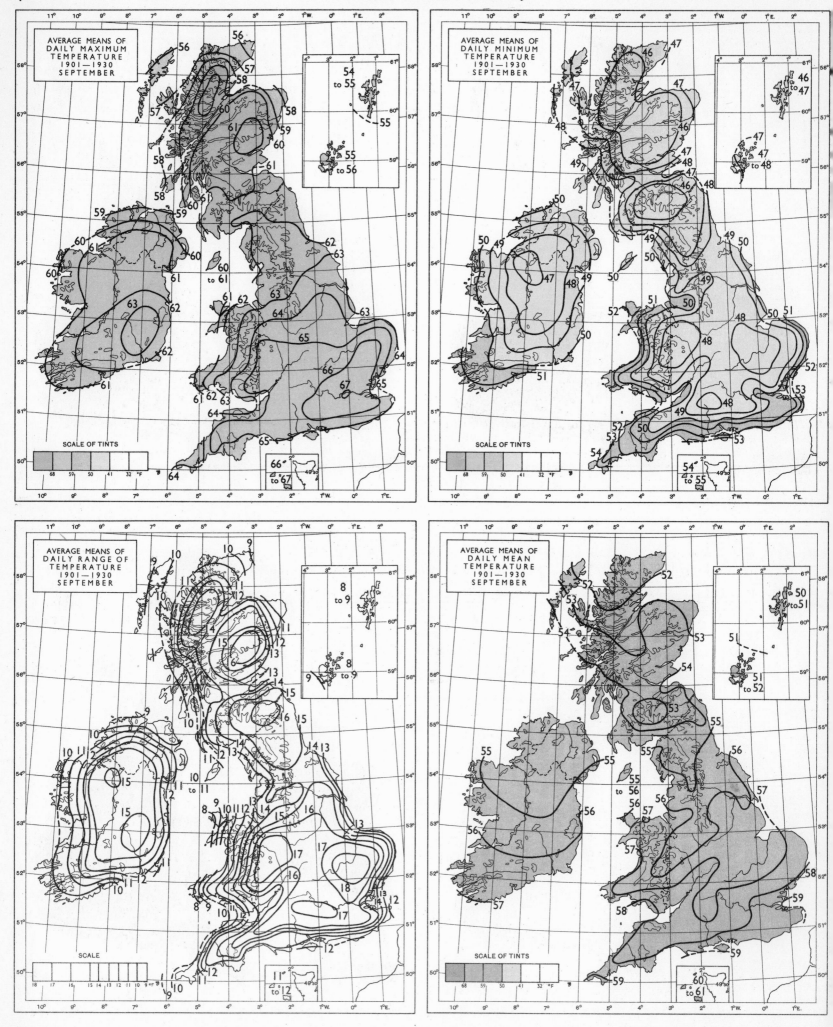

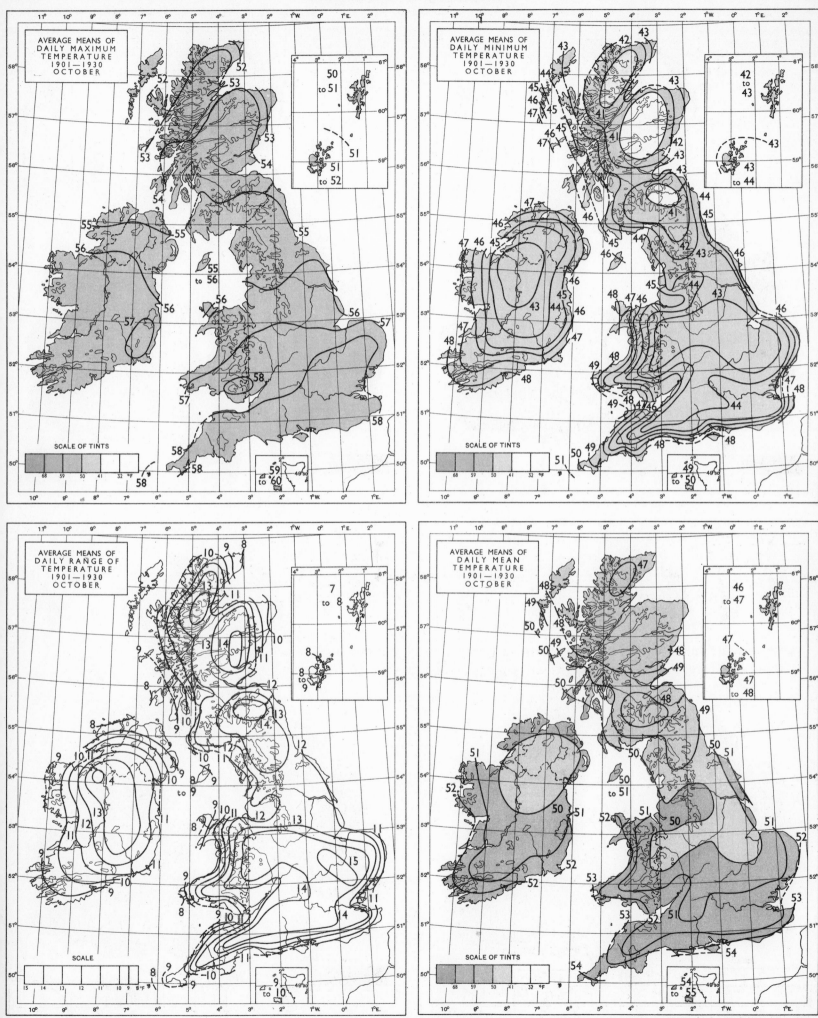

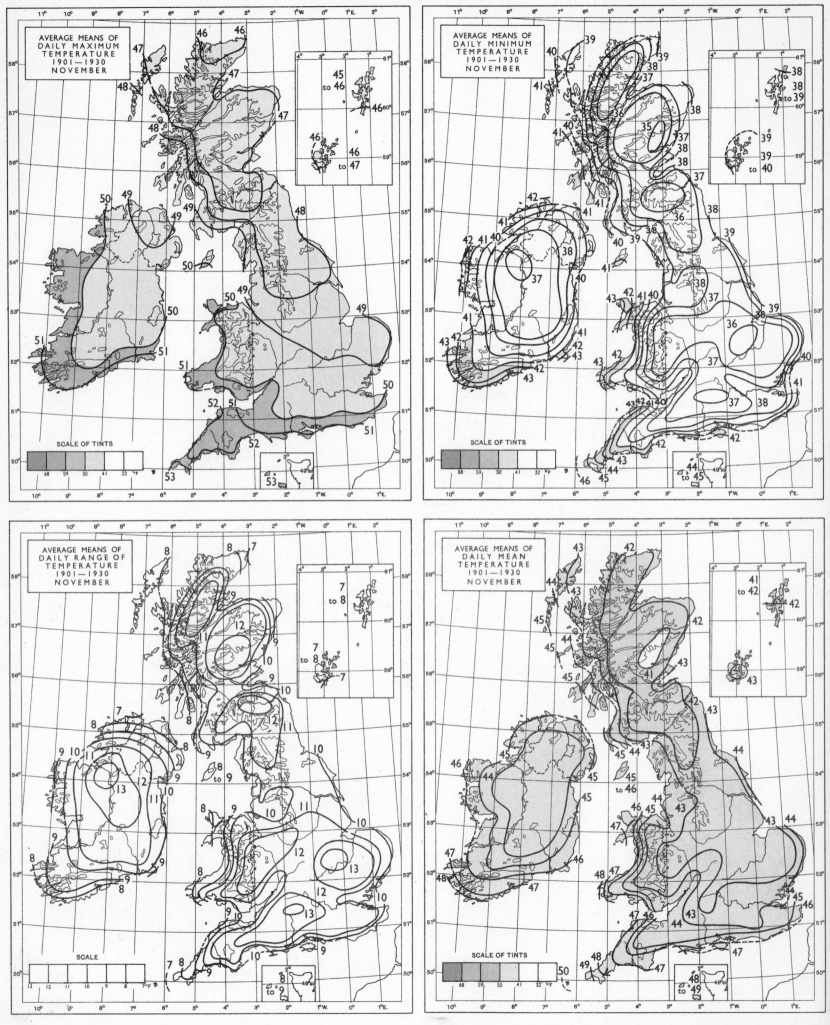

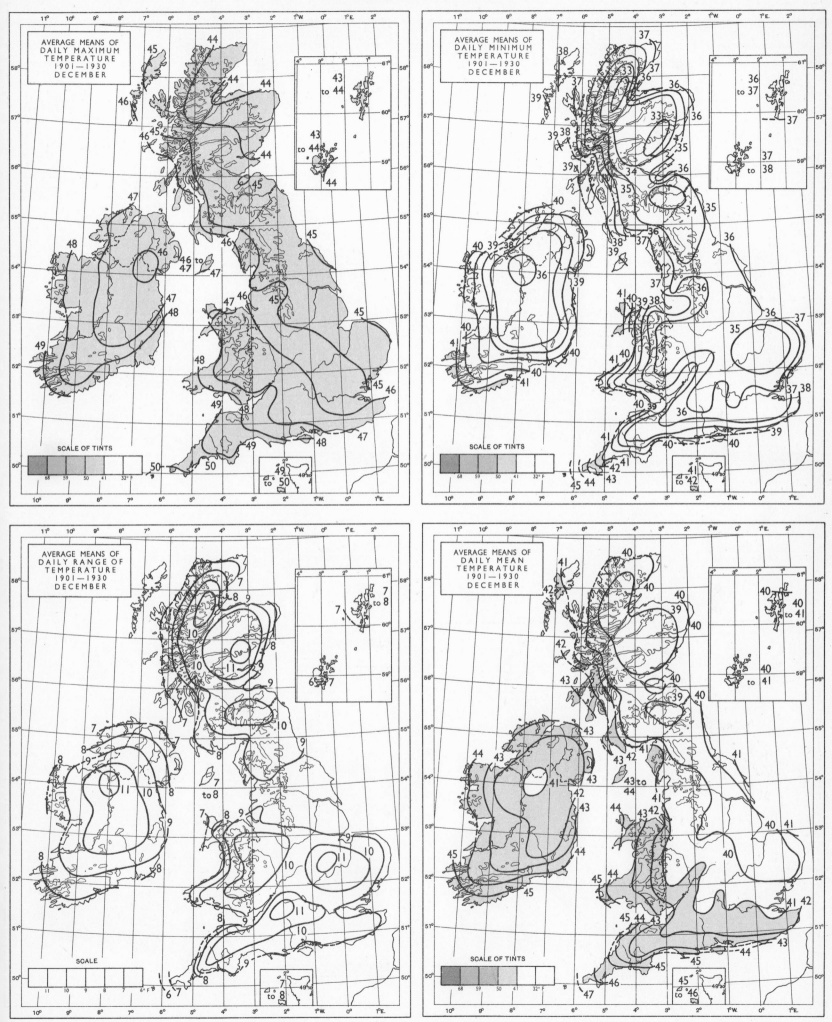

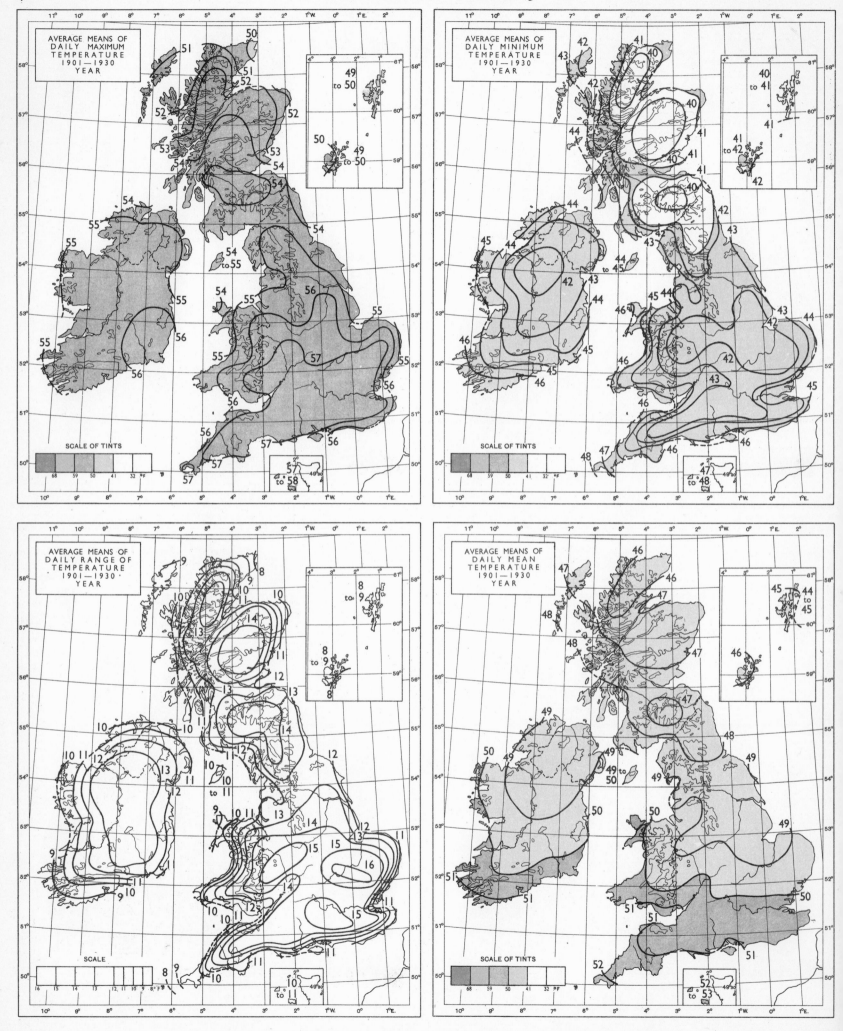

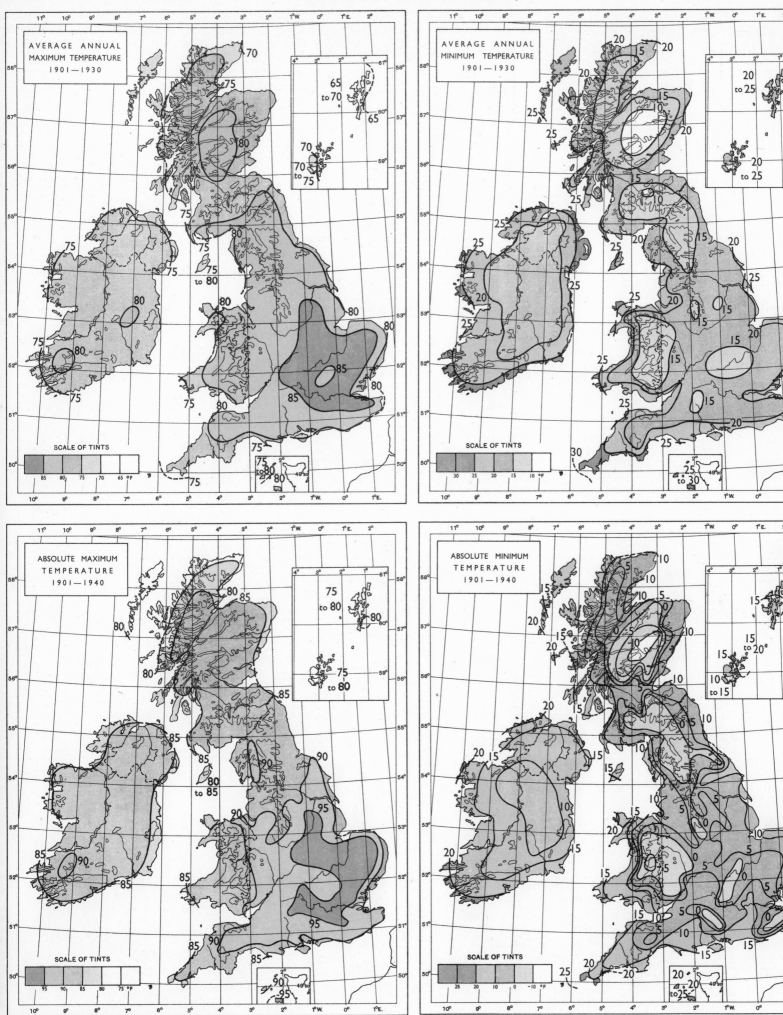

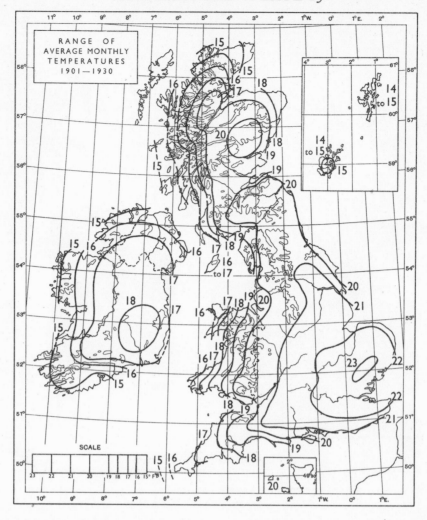

RANGE OF
AVERAGE MONTHLY
TEMPERATURES
1901—1930

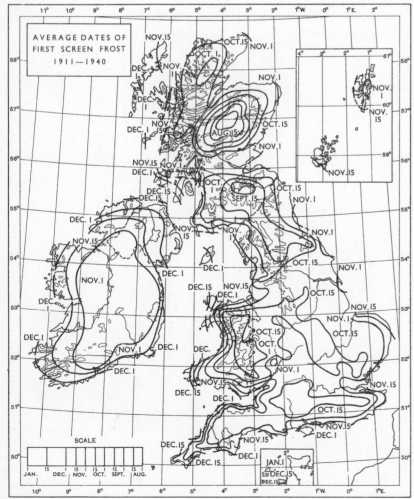

AVERAGE DATES OF
FIRST SCREEN FROST
1911—1940

AVERAGE DATES OF
LAST SCREEN FROST
1911—1940

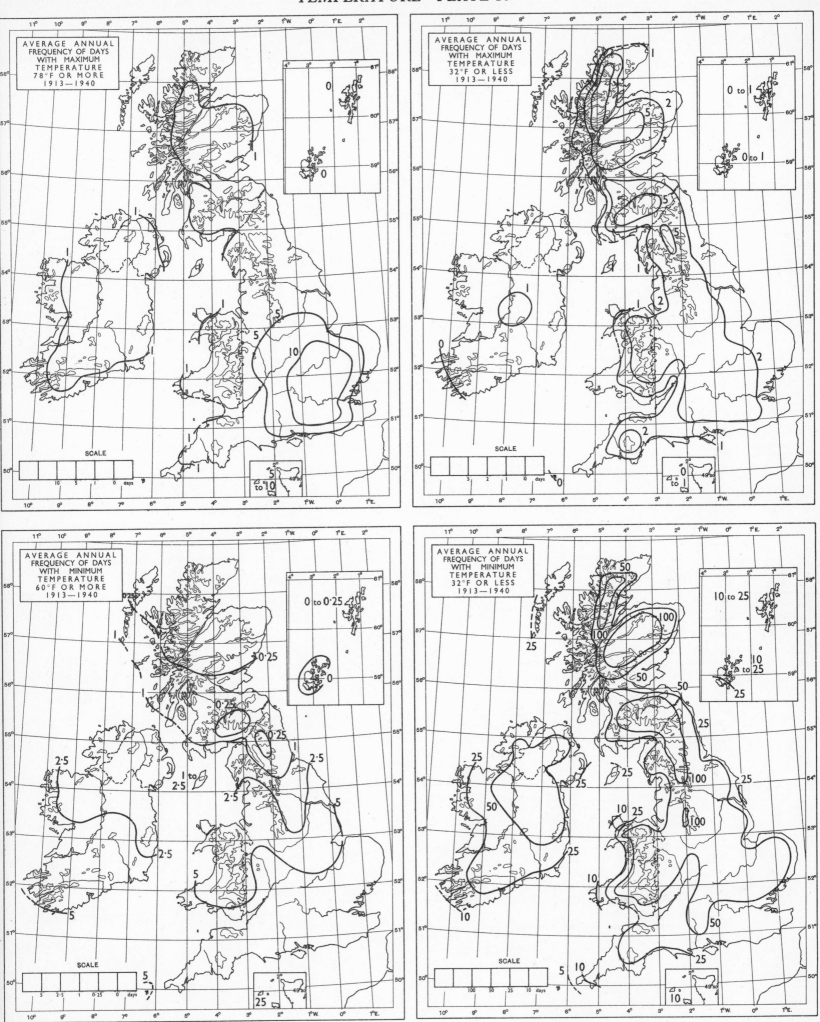

ANNUAL VARIATION OF AVERAGE TEMPERATURE

Jan. Feb. Mar. Apr. May. June. July. Aug. Sept. Oct. Nov. Dec.

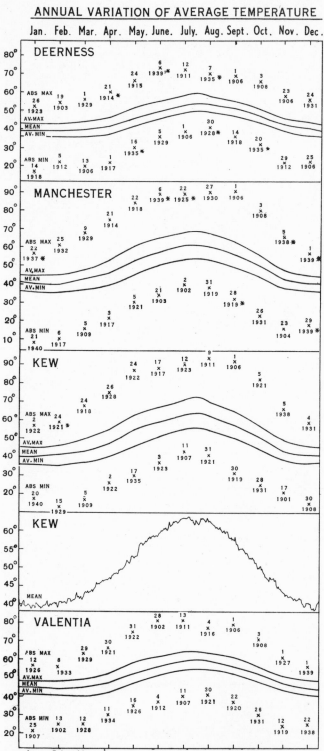

Graphs of Annual Frequency of daily
Maximum and Minimum Temperatures

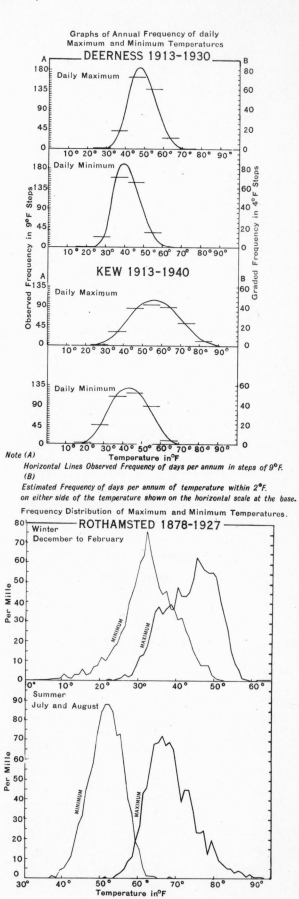

Note (A)
Horizontal Lines Observed Frequency of days per annum in steps of 9°F.
(B)
Estimated Frequency of days per annum of temperature within 2°F.
on either side of the temperature shown on the horizontal scale at the base.

Frequency Distribution of Maximum and Minimum Temperatures.

Jan. Feb. Mar. Apr. May. June. July. Aug. Sept. Oct. Nov. Dec.

The smoothed mean curves are based on monthly means of maximum
& minimum temperatures for the period 1901–1930.

The corresponding unsmoothed curve (Kew) is based on daily means for
the period 1871–1940.

The absolute maximum and minimum temperatures are for the period
1901–1940. The dates (year and day) of absolute maximum and
minimum for each month are indicated the day above and the year
below the respective crosses.

✱ Where the year is starred, this date is the most recent of a number
of occasions.

DIURNAL VARIATION OF TEMPERATURE
KEW

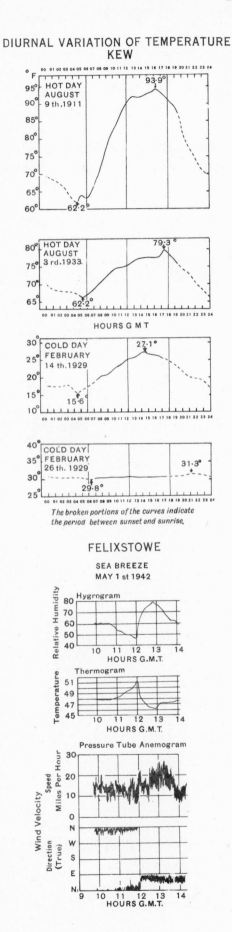

The broken portions of the curves indicate
the period between sunset and sunrise.

FELIXSTOWE

SEA BREEZE
MAY 1st 1942

AVERAGE HOURLY TEMPERATURE

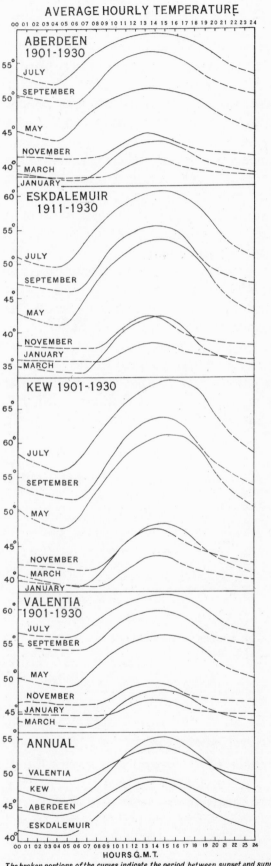

The broken portions of the curves indicate the period between sunset and sunrise.

§4—RAINFALL

INTRODUCTION

The rainfall data used in the compilation of the maps and diagrams have been derived from measurements of precipitation collected in standard rain-gauges on selected sites. These rain-gauges and their maintenance are described in the " Meteorological observer's handbook "[1]*. Rain, drizzle, snow, sleet and hail make up almost all the total rainfall, but there are also small additions due to the deposit of dew, hoar frost, rime or wet fog on the collecting surface of the rain-gauge. The amount of rainfall is expressed in terms of the depth, in inches, of the layer of water which has fallen into the aperture of the gauge since the previous measurement was taken. The " rainfall day " commences at 9h., and the amount which falls during the next 24 hours is credited to that day in the records. The gauge is so designed and exposed that the amount recorded is a good sample of the rain falling on the ground in the immediate vicinity of the gauge. Special steps are taken to measure frozen precipitation, and for information concerning these and all matters of correct exposure of the rain-gauge reference should be made to the Handbook[1].

Self-recording rain-gauges have also been used to give a continuous record of precipitation, and show rate of fall and duration. These are described in the Handbook[1].

A history of early experiments leading to the adoption of the present standard rain-gauges and their exposure has been given by Salter[2].

The geographical distribution of rainfall is indicated in these maps by isohyetal lines, the procedure being similar to that adopted in the " Rainfall atlas of the British Isles "[3].

The data used to compile most of the present rainfall maps and diagrams have already been published in the annual volumes of *British rainfall*, 1901-1930, and articles in these volumes summarize the data in various ways. Table I, which is of general interest, is taken from *British rainfall*, 1937[4].

TABLE I.—GENERAL AVERAGE RAINFALL (INCHES), 1901-1930

	England and Wales in.	Scotland in.	Ireland in.	British Isles in.
January	3·41	5·51	4·57	4·27
February	2·71	4·28	3·81	3·43
March	2·82	3·84	3·47	3·28
April	2·37	3·24	2·82	2·72
May	2·43	3·24	2·93	2·77
June	2·30	2·86	2·75	2·54
July	2·99	3·64	3·36	3·27
August	3·62	4·71	4·35	4·10
September	2·64	4·11	3·29	3·21
October	3·90	5·28	4·47	4·39
November	3·59	5·35	4·31	4·24
December	4·28	5·92	5·09	4·97
Year	37·06	51·98	45·22	43·19

HISTORICAL BACKGROUND

(a) General Annual Rainfall for 222 Years

Estimates of the general annual rainfall experienced over England have been computed by Glasspoole[5] back to the year 1727. The diagram below is based on these values, and illustrates that periods of one or more relatively dry years alternate with relatively wet periods, but without any persistent regularity. The average for the period 1901-1930 over England is shown by the horizontal line ; this average is close to that for the whole period 1727-1948.

* The superior figures refer to the bibliography on page 58.

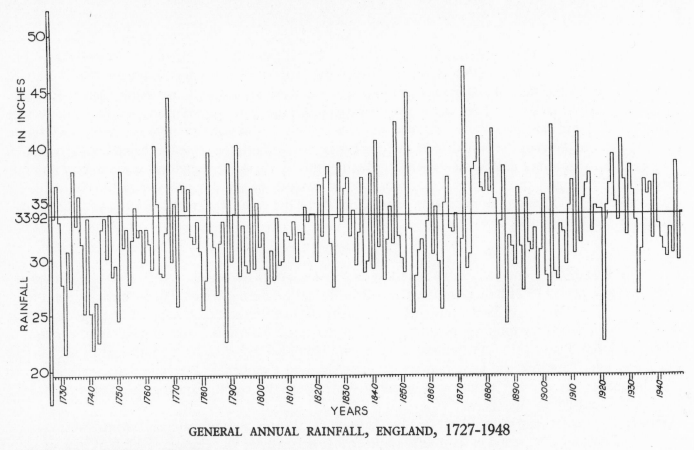

GENERAL ANNUAL RAINFALL, ENGLAND, 1727-1948

(b) Wettest and Driest Months

Table II gives the wettest and driest months on record up to 1940.

TABLE II.—WETTEST AND DRIEST MONTHS OVER THE BRITISH ISLES, 1869-1940

	Jan.	Feb.	Mar.	Apr.	May	June	July	Aug.	Sept.	Oct.	Nov.	Dec.	Year
Wettest	1928	1923	1903	1882	1924	1872	1936	1917	1918	1903	1940	{1876 / 1914}	1872
Driest	1880	1932	1929	1938	1896	1925	1913	1940	1910	{1879 / 1922}	1896	1933	1887

This table defines the extreme month and year over the British Isles generally, but rainfall is so variable that an individual station may record its largest total in the same year that another station experiences its smallest[6].

PLATES 1-13

MAPS OF AVERAGE MONTHLY AND ANNUAL RAINFALL, 1901-1930.—In the preparation of these maps the average monthly and annual rainfall for 1901-1930 for 69 representative stations was first computed. These values were then compared with the corresponding averages for the same stations for the period 1881-1915, and the values for 1901-1930 as a percentage of those for 1881-1915 were plotted to give isopercental maps. These were then used to adjust the 1881-1915 maps [3, 7] to the 1901-1930 values, and these adjusted maps are now presented. Details of the process have been published in *British rainfall*, 1937[4].

The maps make it clear that average rainfall is controlled by the configuration of the ground and the distance from the Atlantic Ocean. Both on the monthly and annual maps this geographical distribution is well marked. In the amounts of rainfall, however, there are appreciable differences in the averages from month to month and from season to season, as well as from place to place.

PLATE 14

DIAGRAMS OF AVERAGE MONTHLY RAINFALL AT SELECTED STATIONS, 1901-1930.—The diagrams show the average monthly rainfall, 1901-1930, for 28 representative stations. The stations on the left are to the west of the main land masses, while those on the right are in the east of Scotland, England, Wales or Ireland. The stations are arranged down the plate from north to south. The average annual rainfall and the altitude are indicated for each station. Whereas the maps on Plates 1-13 aim at defining the variations of the rainfall over the country in each month, the diagrams bring out the variation from month to month at individual stations. The monthly averages for individual stations vary appreciably in different periods. There is no indication of smooth or regular progression in amount from month to month, although the maximum rainfall occurs in the early winter in the west, and the rainfall is least in the spring in all areas.

PLATES 15-18

MAPS OF AVERAGE MONTHLY AND ANNUAL NUMBER OF RAIN-DAYS, 1901-1930.—A rain-day is defined as a period of 24 hours, commencing normally at 9h., during which 0·01 inch or more of rain is recorded. The maps have been constructed from the data of 265 stations, selected to be as uniformly distributed over the country as possible. The distribution resembles that shown on the maps of average rainfall, Plates 1-13, but the frequency of rain-days also increases from south-east to north-west. On the whole, June has the least number of rain-days and October or December the greatest. The distribution of the average annual and monthly values over the country during the period 1881-1915 has been discussed by Glasspoole[8, 9].

In addition to the rain-days, illustrated by these maps, there is another category termed wet-days. A wet-day is defined as a period of 24 hours, commencing normally at 9h., during which 0·04 inch or more of rain is recorded. Maps showing the distribution of the number of wet-days have been published annually in *British rainfall* since 1919. Comparison of the annual number of wet-days with that of rain-days shows that in the Midlands of England the former is about 65 per cent. of the latter ; the proportion reaches 90 per cent. in the mountainous districts of north-west Ireland and western Scotland[8].

PLATES 19 AND 20

MAPS OF MEAN DEVIATION OF MONTHLY AND ANNUAL RAINFALL, 1881-1915.—Plate 19 shows these maps for January[10], April, July and October, and the first map on Plate 20 is the annual one[11]. The mean deviations were obtained by expressing the rainfall for each station for each of the named months and for each year of the 35 years as a percentage of the corresponding average (monthly or yearly), then taking the arithmetical departure of such a percentage from 100 irrespective of sign, summing these departures and dividing by 35, the number of years.

Table III gives the most likely distribution of monthly rainfalls. Both the mean deviation in the left-hand column and the rainfall amounts at the head of the table are expressed as percentages of the average monthly fall. Each entry in the body of the table gives the number of occasions (in 100 years) on which the rainfall for a single specified month may be expected to lie within the limits shown at the head of the column.

This Table is for use in conjunction with the maps of Plate 19. Suppose, for example, that it is required to know the chance in October of a rainfall of twice the average at Blackpool. The mean deviation is seen from the October map to be 30 per cent. so that the second row of the Table applies. The percentage frequency of amounts greater than 200 per cent. is 0·5 + 0·1 = 0·6, and thus an October rainfall of more than twice the average amount at Blackpool is likely to occur only about six times in a thousand years. At Durham for July, however, the mean deviation is as much as 50 per cent. ; and so we find (by adding the columns to the right of that headed " 176-200 ") that more than twice the average fall may be expected once in 15 years ; also, a fall of 25 per cent. or less is likely in one year in nine (11 per cent.).

TABLE III.—PERCENTAGE FREQUENCIES OF MONTHLY RAINFALL

Rainfall for a single month expressed as a percentage of the average monthly fall

Mean deviation	0–25	26–50	51–75	76–100	101–125	126–150	151–175	176–200	201–225	226–250	251–275	276–300	Over 300
25	1·7	5	14	27	31	17	4						
30	1·7	7	18	25	24	15	7	2	0·5	0·1			
35	3	9	18	23	20	14	7	4	1·5	0·4	0·1		
40	6	11	17	20	18	13	8	4	2	0·9	0·3	0·1	
45	9	11	16	18	16	12	8	5	3	1·4	0·7	0·2	0·1
50	11	11	15	16	15	12	8	5	3	2	1·0	0·5	0·1
55	14	11	14	15	13	11	8	6	4	2	1·3	0·6	0·5
60	16	10	13	14	12	11	8	6	4	3	1·6	0·9	0·8

MAP OF AVERAGE ANNUAL NUMBER OF DAYS WITH 0·4 INCH OR MORE OF RAIN.—This map is based on the records of 24 stations of long standing, covering at least 30 years and in some cases as many as 61 years[12], together with information given in the Annual Summary of the *Monthly weather report*. Investigation showed that for any given place the number of days with 0·4 inch or more of rain equals the annual rainfall in inches less 8. This equation was used to amplify the distribution shown on the map.

GRAPH OF AVERAGE ANNUAL NUMBER OF DAYS WITH RAIN EXCEEDING SPECIFIED AMOUNTS. —The graph illustrates the increase in this number of days with the increase in average annual rainfall. For example, the numbers of days a year with 1·0 inch or more are for the four stations shown, 1·5, 5·0, 14·0, and 45·0, the corresponding average annual rainfall amounts being 23·8, 46·5, 77·8 and 130·1 inches. The four curves can be used to give a first approximation to the frequency of the average number of days with rainfall exceeding any specified amount up to 2 inches at stations in the British Isles where the average annual rainfall is between 24 and 130 inches.

GRAPHS OF FREQUENCY OF MONTHLY AND ANNUAL TOTALS OF RAINFALL OF SPECIFIED AMOUNTS, OXFORD, 1845-1944.—In the diagram of actual frequencies for the year, the heights of the columns show, by the vertical scale on the left, how many times in 100 years the annual rainfall has given the number of inches shown on the horizontal scale at the foot. Thus the total was between 14·00 and 14·99 inches in one year, between 17·00 and 17·99 inches in 4 years, and so on. The shape of this diagram is rather irregular, because 100 years is not sufficient to smooth out the accidental irregularities. The diagram for the next 100 years would be similar in its general outline, but even if the climate remained unchanged, it would differ in detail. The smooth curve is an attempt to show the frequency distribution which would be given by a very long series of observations, long enough for the accidental irregularities to cancel out. It is the normal frequency curve, adjusted slightly to allow for the fact that the distribution is not quite symmetrical about the mean ; it is calculated from the mean and the squares and cubes of the departures from the mean.

The diagrams and curves for the four months January, April, July and October are to be interpreted in the same way, except that the columns refer to monthly totals of 0-0·24 inch, 0·25-0·49 inch, and so on. The process of curve-fitting adopted is the same as for the year. It is not strictly appropriate for the monthly totals, where the lower limit of rainfall is zero, but it is sufficiently accurate for practical purposes ; the actual frequency distributions are so irregular that the labour involved in fitting a more elaborate type of curve would not have been justified.

Both the diagrams and curves bring out clearly the main characteristics of the variation from year to year, namely, that there was a lack of symmetry of the distributions, which was much greater for the monthly than for the annual totals, and that the greatest total in each month was considerably more than twice the mean.   The range was large in October, relatively small in April, and intermediate in January and July.

PLATE 21

MAPS OF AN EXTREMELY DRY MONTH, FEBRUARY 1932, AND AN EXTREMELY WET MONTH, DECEMBER 1914.—These maps show the monthly fall in inches recorded in February 1932 and December 1914, months which were respectively extremely dry and extremely wet over the British Isles as a whole.   The general rainfall in February 1932 was only 0·5 inch (13 per cent. of the average) and in December 1914 was 8·6 inches (183 per cent. of the average).   The period represented is 1870-1943.   Two other months in that period were outstanding : April 1938 was about as dry as February 1932 and December 1876 about as wet as December 1914.

No rain was recorded at several stations in the following months :—February of 1891, 1895, 1932 and 1934, March of 1929 and 1931, April of 1893, 1912 and 1938, June of 1921, 1925 and 1942, July of 1911, August of 1940 and September of 1894.   In June 1925 there was no measurable rain over an area of some 6,410 square miles in southern England and Wales, and in February 1891 over some 3,290 square miles in central and east England and south Wales.

MAPS OF AVERAGE ANNUAL RAINFALL, 1881-1915, OVER LONDON AND OVER THE CENTRAL ENGLISH LAKE DISTRICT.—These maps define in detail the probable distribution of average annual rainfall over London and the central English Lake District[13].

DIAGRAM SHOWING RELATION OF RAINFALL TO CONFIGURATION ACROSS NORTHERN ENGLAND, 1881-1915.—This diagram shows the configuration and rainfall along the line indicated on the rainfall map of the central English Lake District.   It illustrates the general relation of rainfall to topography and shows that the increase of rain with altitude decreases from west to east, that the valleys often receive a rainfall more appropriate to the surrounding hills, and that the maximum rainfall is rather to the leeward of the summits of the mountains.   The average amount of rainfall at any station is dependent upon the vertical component of the prevailing winds and the amount of moisture remaining to be condensed after these winds have passed over the land from the sea.   Thus Seathwaite, in the valley to the south of Derwent Water, with an average annual rainfall of 122 inches and altitude of 423 feet, owes its high rainfall to its position to the north-east of Great Gable.

PLATES 22 AND 23

MAPS OF HEAVY FALLS OF RAIN OF AUGUST 25-26, 1912; OCTOBER 26-28, 1909; DECEMBER 30, 1900; JUNE 16, 1917; AUGUST 24-25, 1891; JUNE 28, 1917; JUNE 23-24, 1911; JULY 7, 1916 AND OCTOBER 11, 1916.—In these maps the unit of time is the rainfall day commencing at 9h.

All rainfall requires the ascent of moist air to higher levels and, by expansion under diminishing pressure, the cooling of such air to below its dew point (the temperature at which the air is saturated). There are three classes of rainfall according to the manner in which this ascent of the damp air is brought about.   These classes are :—(i) *Orographic rain,* the ascent being over sufficiently high ground.   (ii) *Cyclonic rain* associated with the passage of a depression (low pressure system).   There is ascent due to local accumulation (convergence) of the air up to great heights, particularly along the boundary surfaces (fronts) between warm and cold air masses.   (iii) *Convectional* or *instability rain.*   Here the ascent of air is associated with thermal instability due either to surface heating or to inflow of cold air above a layer of warm surface air.

The heaviest rains in this country are rarely due to a single one of these causes acting alone.   On uniform level ground the distribution of rainfall due to the passage of a depression would result mainly from the convergence of the different air masses. The map for August 25-26, 1912 comes near this ideal. In the map for October 26-28, 1909 the distribution due to depressions in the English Channel and southern North Sea is still dominant, but the effect of high ground is seen in Dartmoor, south Wales and the Chilterns. The map for December 30, 1900 also shows a distribution which is dominantly cyclonic, but some orographic effect appears in the areas of heavy rain over the Cotswold and Mendip Hills. On June 23-24, 1911 a depression, moving northwards along the east coast, gave most rain on the eastern slopes of the hills from the Lammermuirs to the Lincolnshire Wolds, but with outliers on the mountains of Cumberland and Wales. The map for July 7, 1916 also shows an intermediate type in which the rainfall, associated with a small depression moving north-east across the country, was heaviest on the south-eastern flanks of the hills to the north of the track. The maps for August 24-25, 1891 and October 11, 1916 show an almost purely topographical effect, due to strong westerly currents associated with depressions to the north. In the former case the belt of strong winds was narrow enough to limit the heavy rain to the Cumbrian Mountains. Purely convectional rain is exemplified in showers or in sporadic and local outbreaks of thundery rain or in local thunderstorms of summer afternoons, an example of which is seen in the map for June 16, 1917. The heaviest thundery rains occur in shallow depressions in summer where there is convergence and the atmosphere is locally very unstable up to great heights. On June 28, 1917 a depression moved up the English Channel, and rain fell in a continuous belt on its northern flank, with local convectional maxima, one of which gave a fall of 9·56 inches at Bruton, Somerset.

MAP OF AVERAGE MAXIMUM DAILY FALL IN A YEAR, MAINLY 1920-1943.—This map has been prepared by plotting the average of the maximum amount recorded in a day over a period of at least 20 of these years at each of 147 stations. A list of the maximum amounts on record is given in *British rainfall*, 1934, the list being limited to the maximum fall in each county, or to falls of four inches or more (in certain counties to 4·50 inches in order not to exceed a reasonable length). Most counties in Ireland, some in the south and east of Scotland and in the Midlands of England have so far not recorded a fall of four inches or more on a rainfall day. The seven entries exceeding eight inches are listed below :—

	In.	*Date.*
Somerset, Bruton (Sexey's School)	9·56	June 28, 1917
„ Cannington (Brymore House) ...	9·40	August 18, 1924
„ Bruton (King's School)	8·48	June 28, 1917
„ Aisholt (Timberscombe)	8·39	June 28, 1917
Glamorgan, Rhondda (Lluest Wen Reservoir) ...	8·31	November 11, 1929
Inverness, Loch Quoich (Kinlochquoich) ...	8·20	October 11, 1916
Cumberland, Borrowdale (Seathwaite)	8·03	November 12, 1897

Details of the largest entries on record in two to seven consecutive days have been given by Hawke[14], and the extreme values are quoted below :—

	In.	*Date.*
Two days Seathwaite	12·42	December 4-5, 1864
Three days „	15·52	December 3-5, 1864
Four days „	16·63	December 3-6, 1864
Five days „	17·91	December 3-7, 1864
Six days „	19·12	December 3-8, 1864
Seven days Ben Nevis	20·57	January 24-30, 1903

PLATE 24

MAP OF GREATEST NUMBER OF CONSECUTIVE DAYS WITHOUT MEASURABLE RAIN, 1887-1947.—This map is based on information published in the annual volumes of *British rainfall* which give the durations of absolute droughts at representative stations. An absolute drought is defined as a period of at least 15 consecutive days, to none of which is credited 0·01 inch of rain or more. The longest well-authenticated absolute droughts covered 60 days within the period March 4 to May 14, 1893, at Hastings, Winchelsea, Lewes and Haywards Heath. In parts of the extreme north of Scotland and the north-west of Ireland no absolute droughts lasting as long as 20 days are on record. On the average, for the period 1906-1947, there is rather more than one absolute drought per year in the south-east of England, but not more than one in five years in parts of the north-west of both Scotland and Ireland.

MAP OF GREATEST NUMBER OF CONSECUTIVE DAYS WITH MEASURABLE RAIN, 1903-1947.—This map, which illustrates the longest rain spells during the period 1903-1947, is based on information published in *British rainfall*. A rain spell is defined as a period of at least 15 consecutive days to each of which is credited 0·01 inch of rain, or more. The longest rain spell on record was of 89 days' duration from August 12 to November 8, 1923, at both Eallabus (Islay) and Ballynahinch Castle, Co. Galway.

MAP OF AVERAGE ANNUAL DURATION OF RAINFALL, 1931-1940.—This map is also based on records published in *British rainfall*. Duration of rainfall is defined as the length of time during which rain fell at a rate of not less than 0·004 inch per hour.

GRAPHS OF AVERAGE HOURLY RAINFALL AT KEW AND VALENTIA, 1871-1920.—These graphs are based upon the averages of the hourly records of rainfall including the occasions when no rain fell. They show that over the year as a whole the total amount of rain during the day approximated to that during the night. In summer, however, there was more rain at night at Valentia than during the day, while at Kew the reverse was the case. In winter there was little variation between day and night at either observatory.

BIBLIOGRAPHY

[1] London, Meteorological Office. Meteorological observers' handbook. London, 1942.

[2] SALTER, M. de C. S.; The rainfall of the British Isles. London (London Univ. Press), 1921.

[3] London, Royal Meteorological Society. Rainfall atlas of the British Isles, London, 1926.

[4] GLASSPOOLE, J.; Rainfall over the British Isles, 1901-1930. *Brit. Rainf., London,* **77,** 1937, p. 264.

[5] GLASSPOOLE, J.; Two centuries of rain. *Met. Mag., London,* **63,** 1928, p. 1.

[6] GLASSPOOLE, J.; The driest and wettest years at individual stations in the British Isles, 1868-1924. *Quart. J.R. met. Soc., London,* **52,** 1926, p. 237.

[7] London, Ordnance Survey Department. Map of average annual rainfall. Great Britain, Sheet 1, Scotland and England north of Kendal; Sheet 2, remainder of England and Wales. London, 1949.

[8] GLASSPOOLE, J.; The distribution over the British Isles in time and space of the annual number of days with rain. *Brit. Rainf., London,* **66,** 1926, p. 260.

[9] GLASSPOOLE, J.; The distribution over the British Isles of the average number of days with rain during each month of the year. *Quart. J.R. met. Soc., London,* **54,** 1928, p. 89.

[10] GLASSPOOLE, J.; The fluctuations of monthly rainfall. *Brit. Rainf., London,* **62,** 1922, p. 234.

[11] GLASSPOOLE, J.; The fluctuations of annual rainfall. *Brit. Rainf., London,* **61,** 1921, p. 288.

[12] BILHAM, E. G. and LLOYD, A. C.; The frequency distribution of daily rainfall. *Brit. Rainf., London,* **72,** 1932, p. 268.

[13] GLASSPOOLE, J.; The average annual rainfall over the county of London. *Brit. Rainf., London,* **73,** 1933, p. 266.

[14] HAWKE, E. L.; Notable falls of rain during intervals of a few days in Great Britain. *Quart. J.R. met. Soc., London,* **68,** 1942, p. 279.

BELASCO, J. E. ; Rainless days of London. *Quart. J.R. met. Soc., London,* **74,** 1948, p. 339.

BROOKS, C. E. P. and GLASSPOOLE, J. ; British floods and droughts, London (Ernest Benn), 1928.

CARRUTHERS, N. ; The optimum period for a British rainfall normal. *Quart. J.R. met. Soc., London,* **71,** 1945, p. 144.

GLASSPOOLE, J. ; The daily fall of rain over the British Isles. *Quart. J.R. met. Soc., London,* **53,** 1927, p. 65.

GLASSPOOLE, J. ; Average and seasonal rainfall over the British Isles. *Trans. Instn Wat. Engrs, London,* **33,** 1928, p. 51.

GLASSPOOLE, J. ; The frequency of rain over the British Isles. *Nature, London,* **121,** 1928, p. 591.

GLASSPOOLE, J. ; The areas covered by intense and widespread falls of rain. *Min. Proc. Instn civ. Engrs, London,* **229,** 1929, p. 137.

GLASSPOOLE, J. ; The reliability of rainfall over the British Isles. *Trans. Instn Wat. Engrs, London,* **35,** 1930, p. 174 and *J. Instn Wat. Engrs, London,* **1,** 1947, p. 441.

GLASSPOOLE, J. ; Heavy falls of rain in short periods (two hours or less). *Quart. J.R. met. Soc., London,* **57,** 1931, p. 57.

GLASSPOOLE, J. ; The wettest places in the British Isles. *Wat. & Wat. Engng, London,* **33,** 1931, p. 560.

GLASSPOOLE, J. ; The rainfall over the British Isles of each of the eleven decades during the period 1820-1929. *Quart. J.R. met. Soc., London,* **59,** 1933, p. 253.

GLASSPOOLE, J. ; The drought over England and Wales during the years 1932-1935. *Trans. Instn Wat. Engrs, London,* **40,** 1935, p. 190.

GLASSPOOLE, J. ; Variation in annual, seasonal and monthly rainfall over the British Isles, 1870-1939. *Quart. J.R. met. Soc., London,* **67,** 1941, p. 5.

GLASSPOOLE, J. ; Rainfall over the British Isles during the decade 1930-1939. *Quart. J.R. met. Soc., London,* **69,** 1943, p. 205.

LEWIS, L. F. ; The seasonal and geographical distribution of absolute drought in England. *Quart. J.R. met. Soc., London,* **65,** 1939, p. 367.

London, Meteorological Office. The book of normals of meteorological elements for the British Isles for periods ending 1915. Section I, Monthly normals for stations (1881-1915). London, 1919. Section V, Monthly normals of rainfall. London, 1924.

McCLEAN, W. N. ; Windermere Basin : rainfall, run-off and storage. *Quart. J.R. met. Soc., London,* **66,** 1940, p. 337.

MILL, H. R. ; Rate of rainfall at Seathwaite. *Quart. J.R. met. Soc., London,* **31,** 1905, p. 229.

MILL, H. R. and SALTER, M. de C. S. ; Isomeric rainfall maps of the British Isles. *Quart. J.R. met. Soc., London,* **41,** 1915, p. 1.

SALTER, M. de C. S. and GLASSPOOLE, J. ; The fluctuations of annual rainfall in the British Isles considered cartographically. *Quart. J.R. met. Soc., London,* **49,** 1923, p. 207.

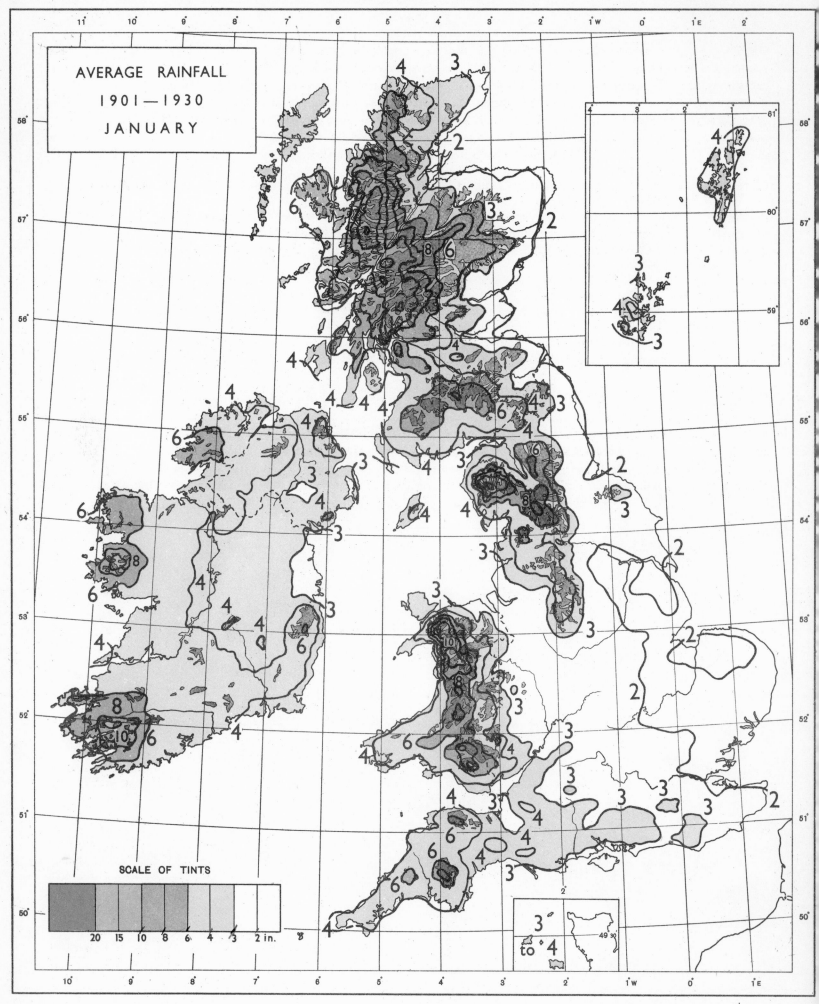

AVERAGE RAINFALL
1901—1930
JANUARY

SCALE OF TINTS

20 15 10 8 6 4 3 2 in.

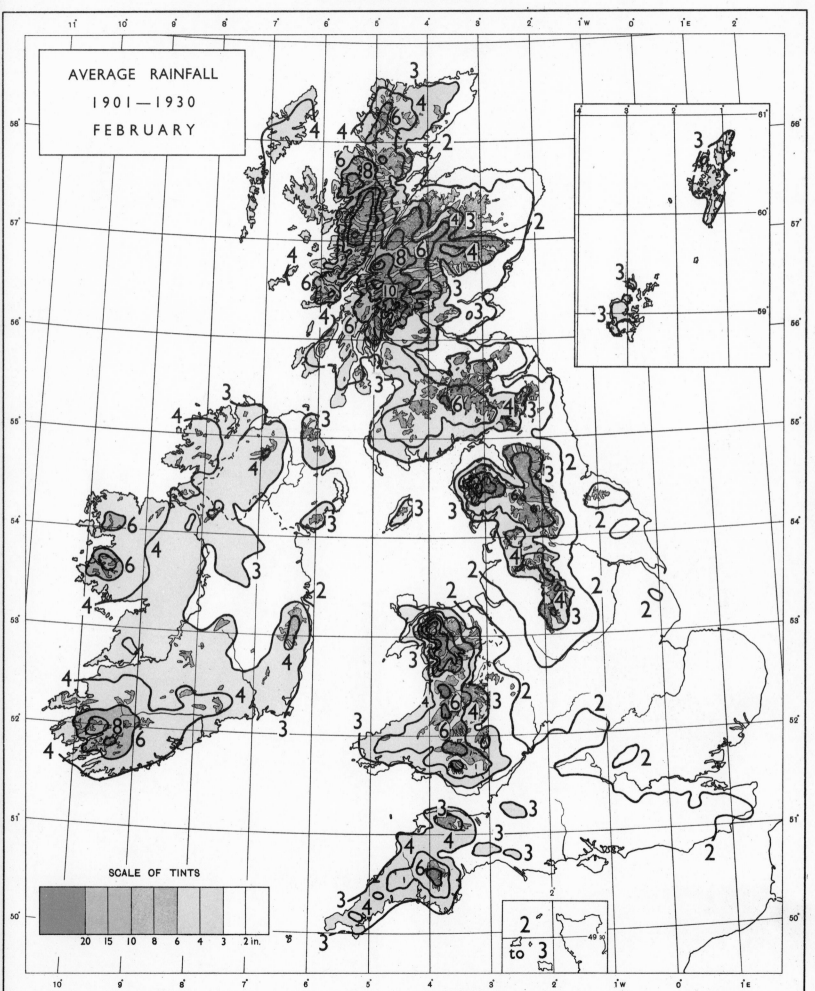

AVERAGE RAINFALL
1901—1930
FEBRUARY

SCALE OF TINTS

20   15   10   8   6   4   3   2 in.

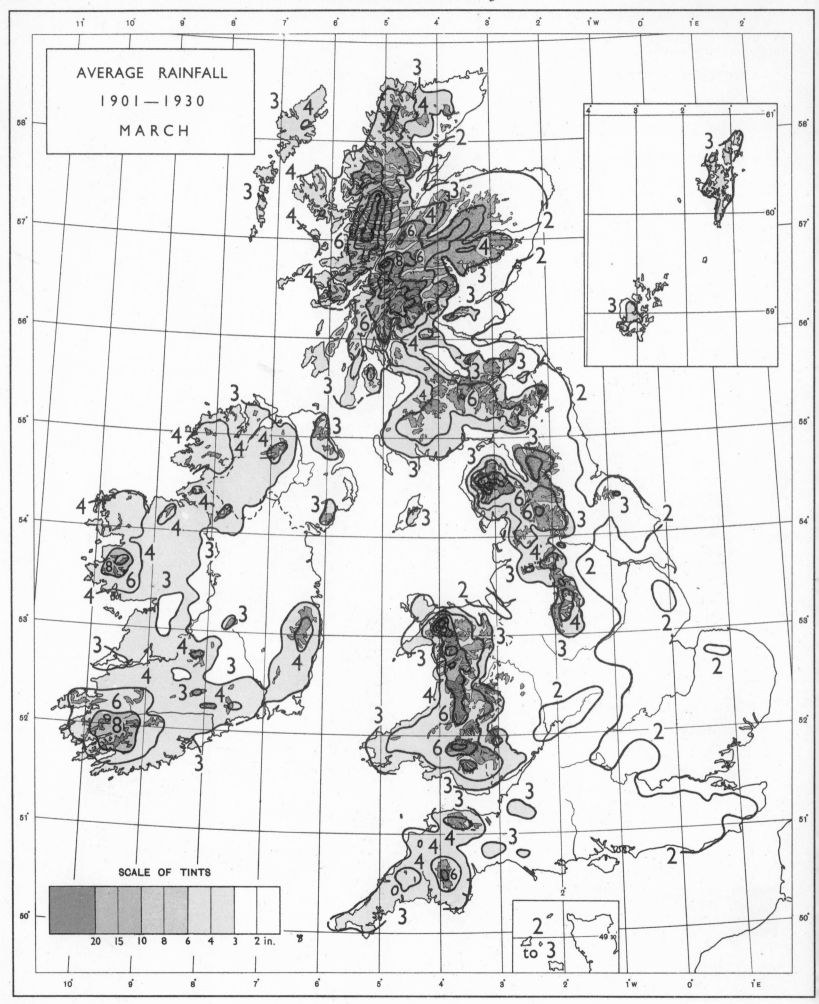

AVERAGE RAINFALL
1901—1930
MARCH

SCALE OF TINTS

20   15   10   8   6   4   3   2 in.

2 to 3

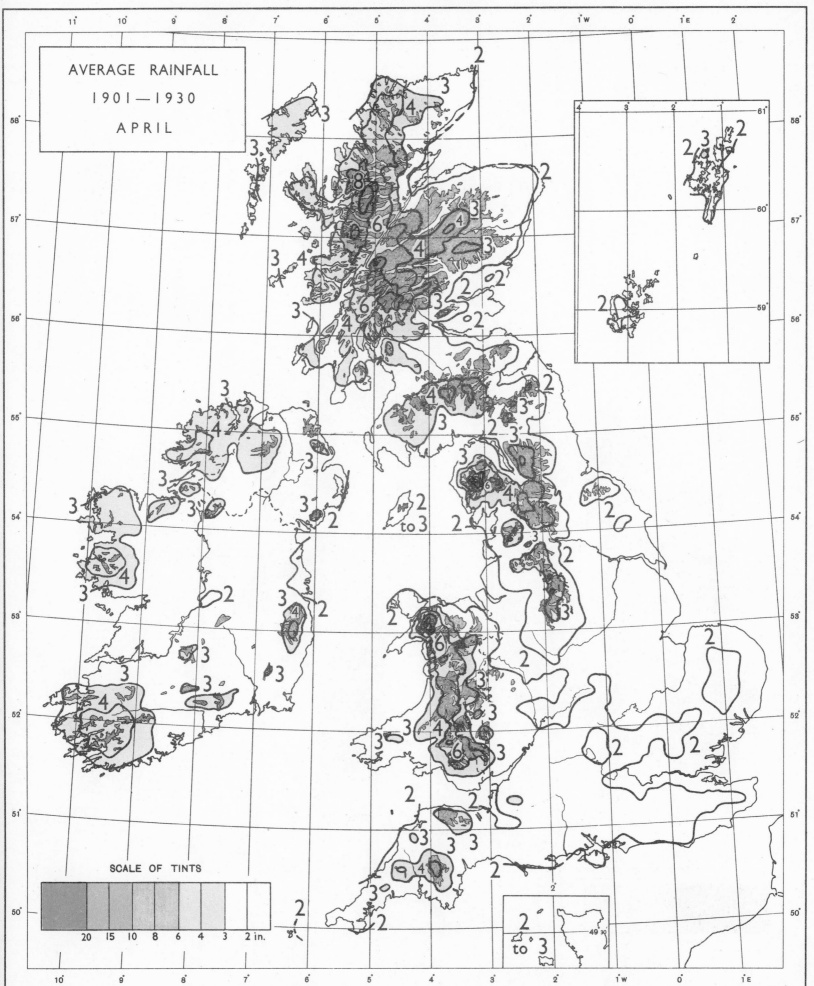

AVERAGE RAINFALL
1901—1930
APRIL

SCALE OF TINTS

20 15 10 8 6 4 3 2 in.

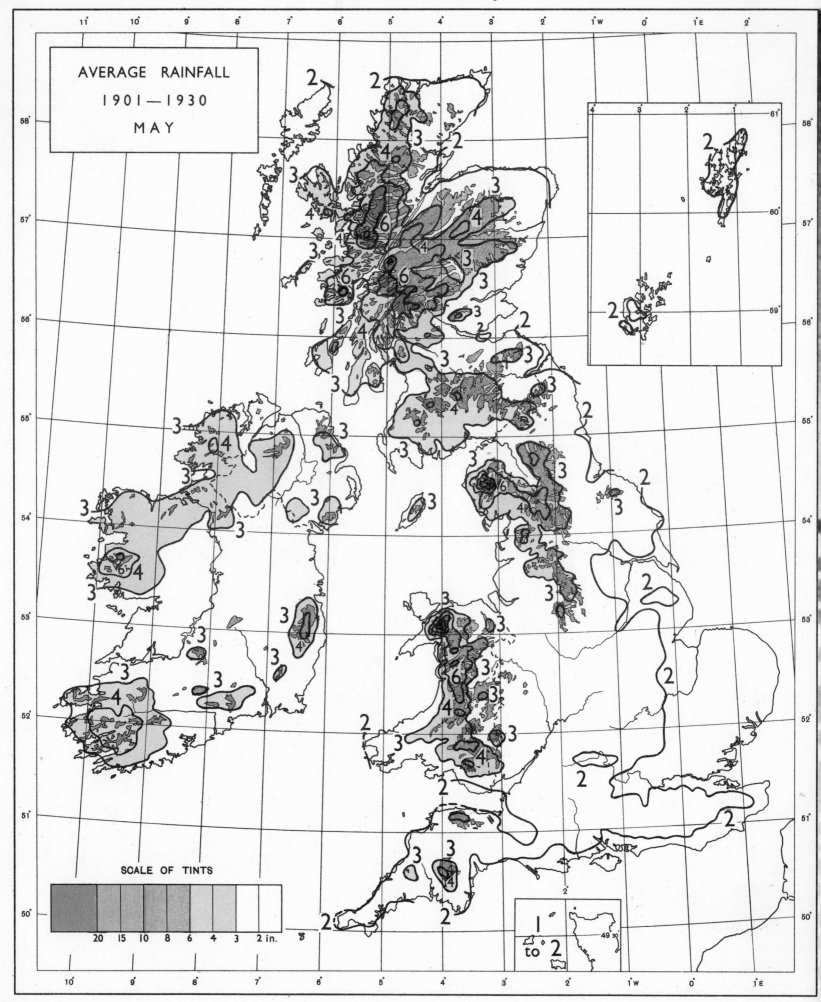

AVERAGE RAINFALL
1901—1930
MAY

SCALE OF TINTS

20   15   10   8   6   4   3   2 in.

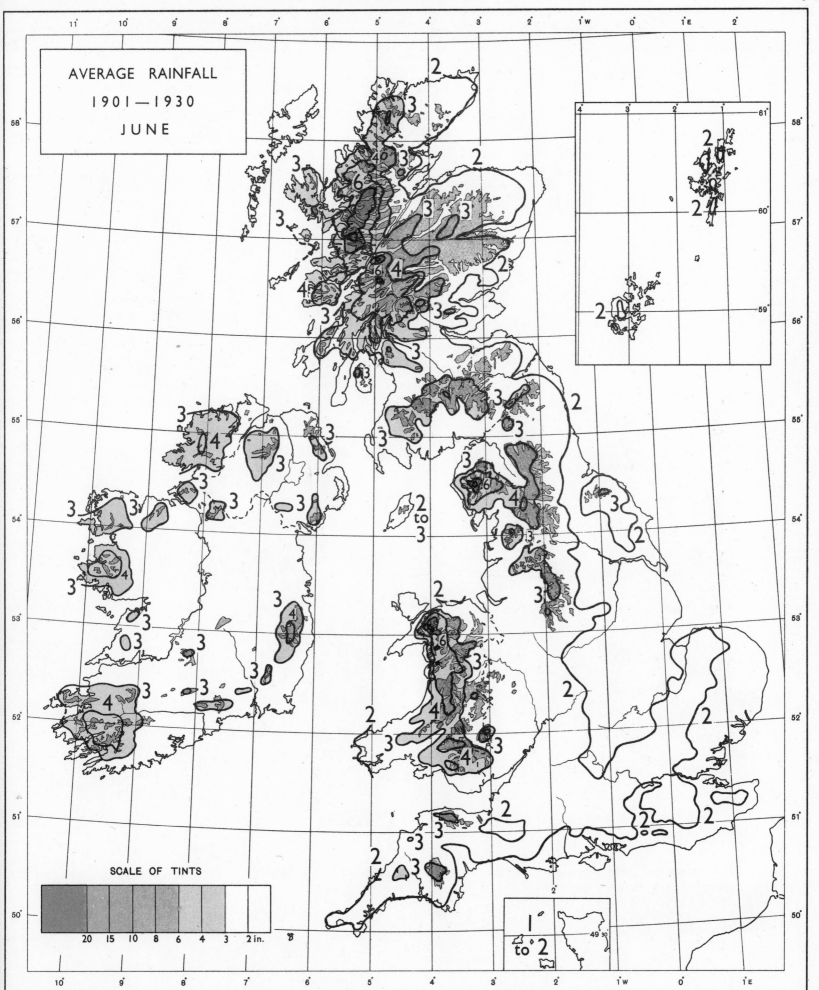

AVERAGE RAINFALL
1901—1930
JUNE

SCALE OF TINTS
20 15 10 8 6 4 3 2 in.

1'
to 2

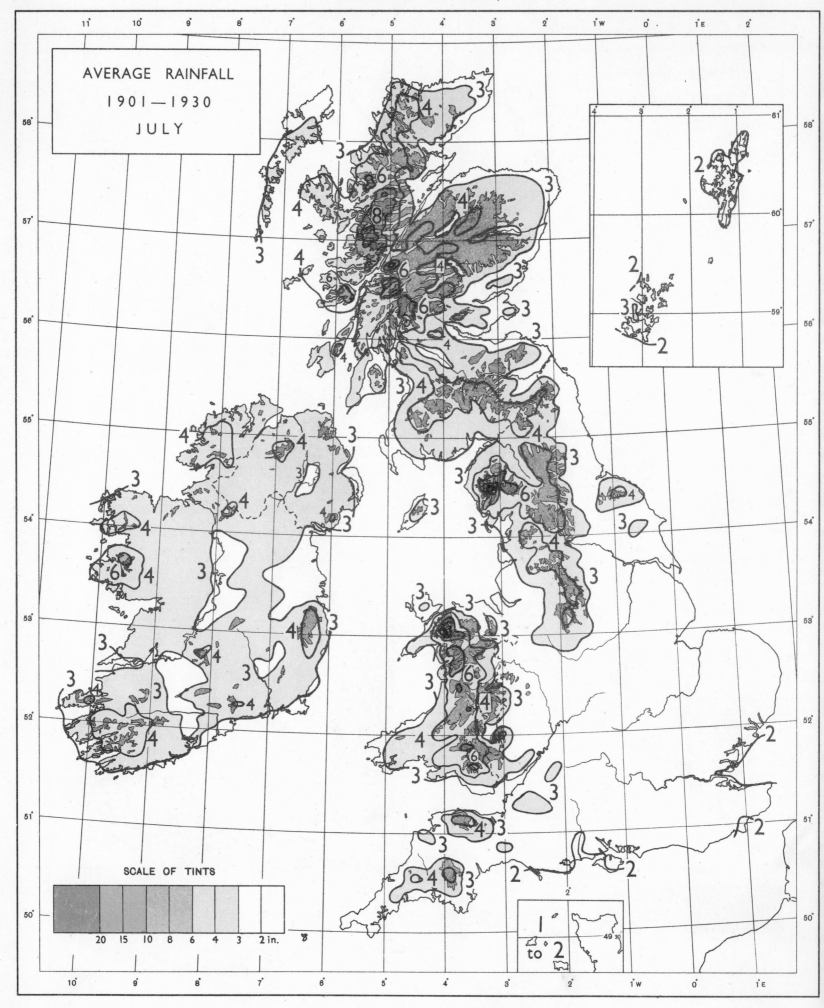

AVERAGE RAINFALL
1901—1930
JULY

SCALE OF TINTS

20 15 10 8 6 4 3 2 in.

1
to
2

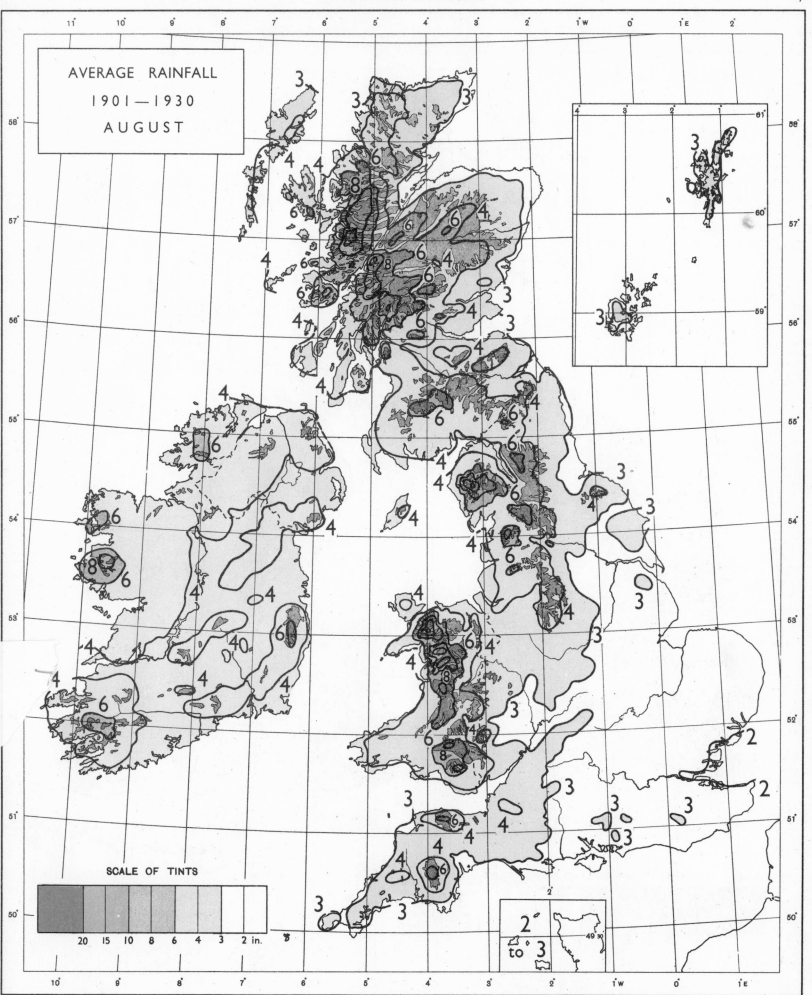

AVERAGE RAINFALL
1901—1930
AUGUST

SCALE OF TINTS

20 15 10 8 6 4 3 2 in.

2
to 3

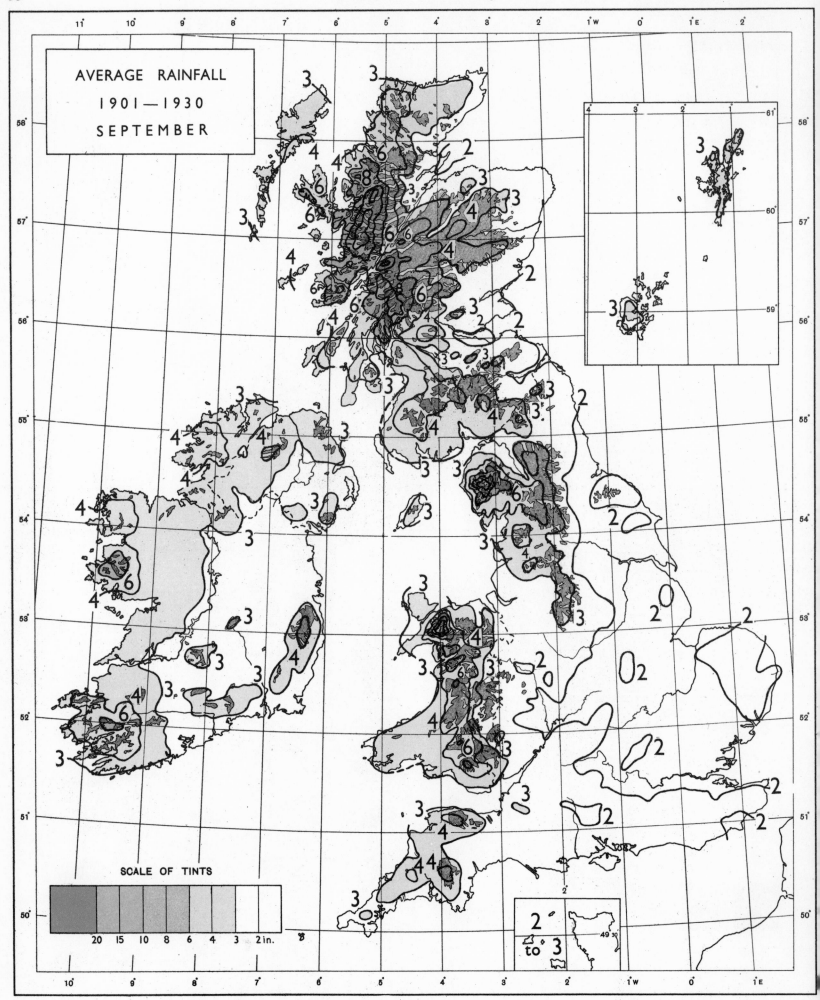

AVERAGE RAINFALL
1901—1930
SEPTEMBER

SCALE OF TINTS

20   15   10   8   6   4   3   2 in.

2 to 3

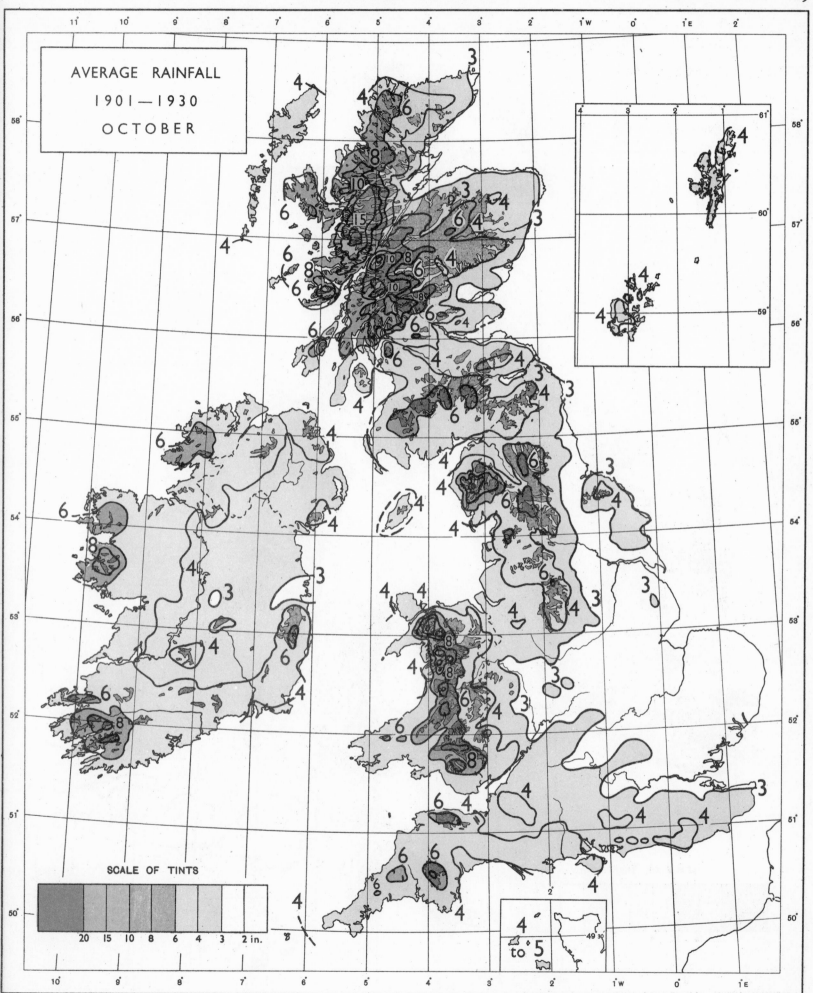

AVERAGE RAINFALL
1901—1930
OCTOBER

SCALE OF TINTS

20 15 10 8 6 4 3 2 in.

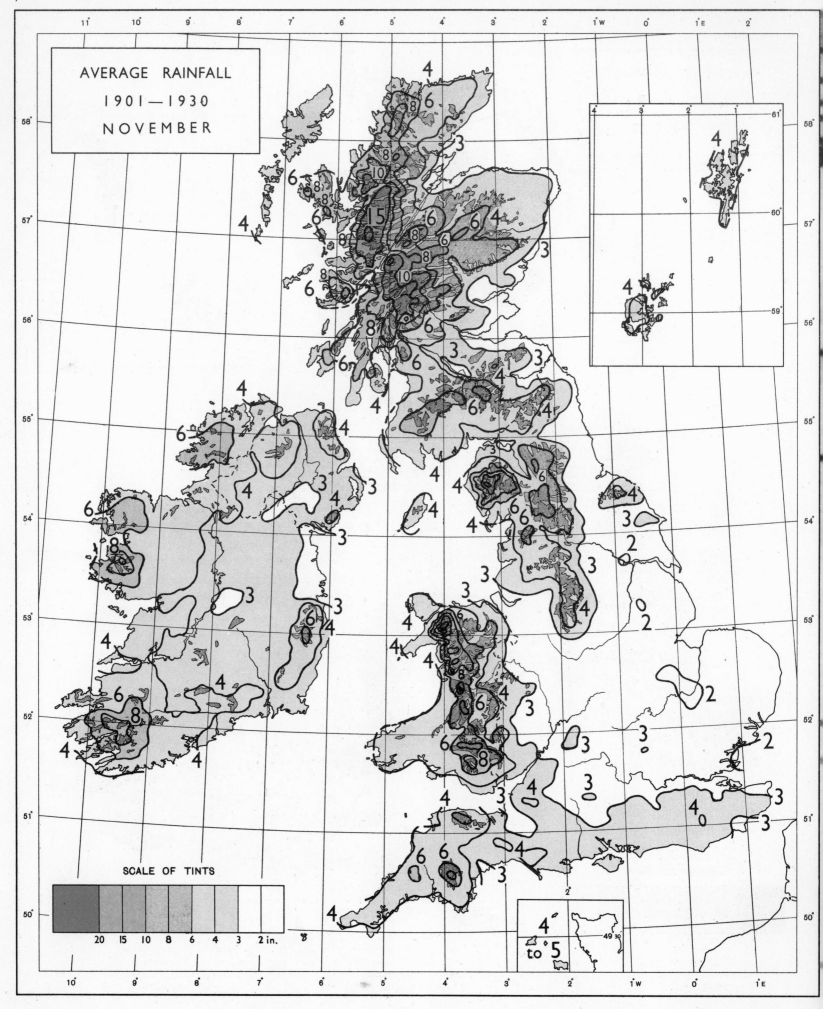

AVERAGE RAINFALL
1901—1930
NOVEMBER

SCALE OF TINTS

20 15 10 8 6 4 3 2 in.

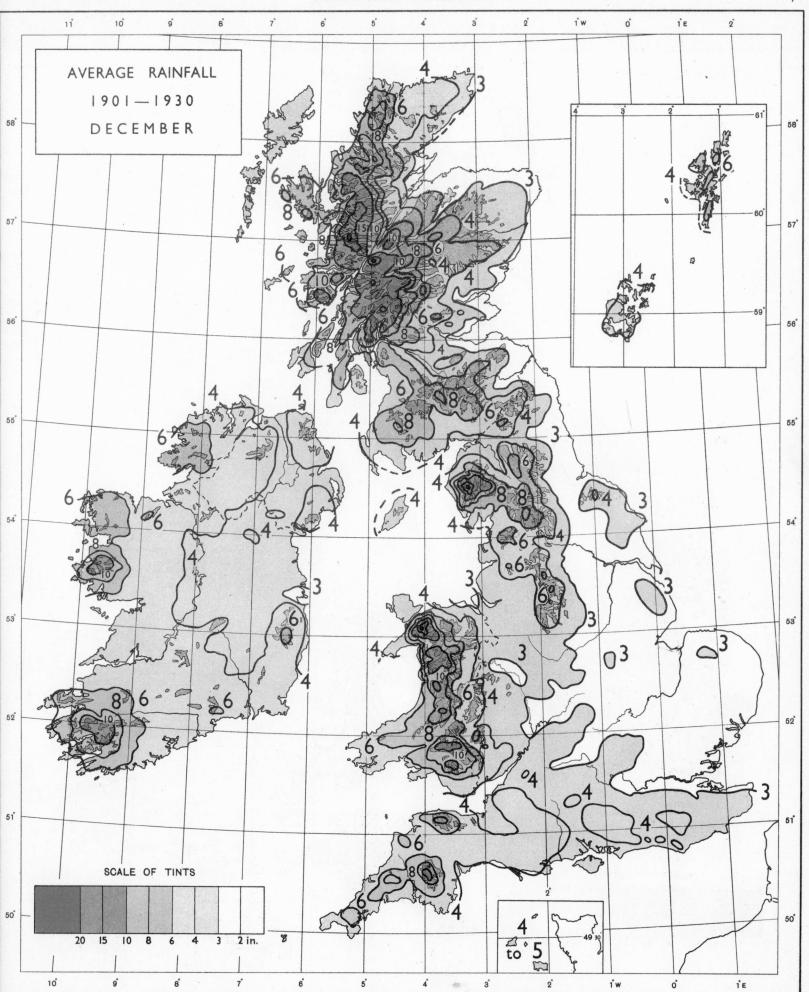

AVERAGE RAINFALL
1901—1930
DECEMBER

SCALE OF TINTS

20 15 10 8 6 4 3 2 in.

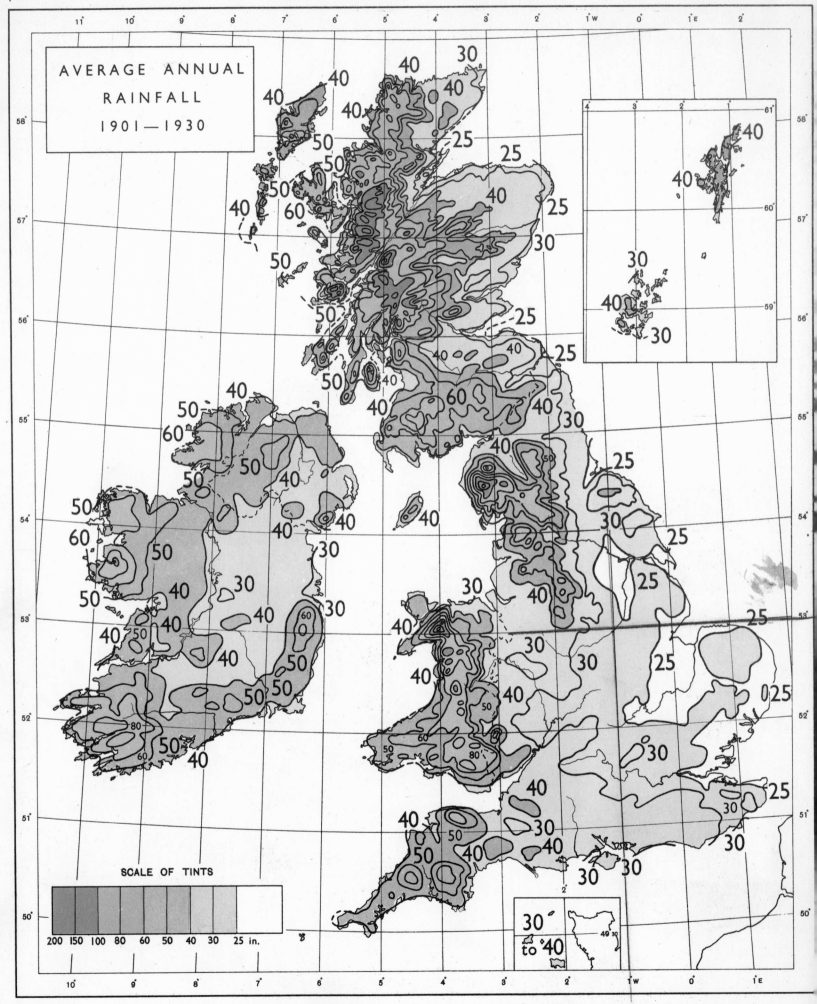

AVERAGE ANNUAL
RAINFALL
1901—1930

SCALE OF TINTS

200 150 100 80 60 50 40 30 25 in.

30
to 40

AVERAGE MONTHLY AND ANNUAL RAINFALL IN INCHES (1901-1930) AT SELECTED STATIONS

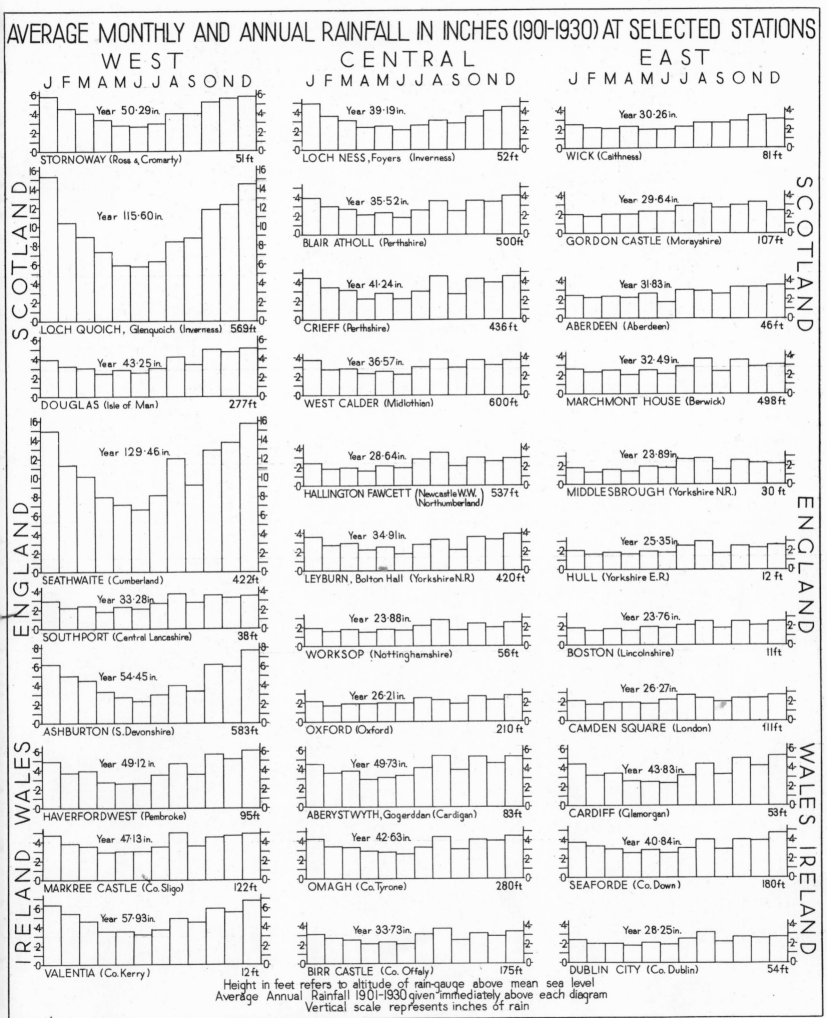

Height in feet refers to altitude of rain-gauge above mean sea level
Average Annual Rainfall 1901-1930 given immediately above each diagram
Vertical scale represents inches of rain

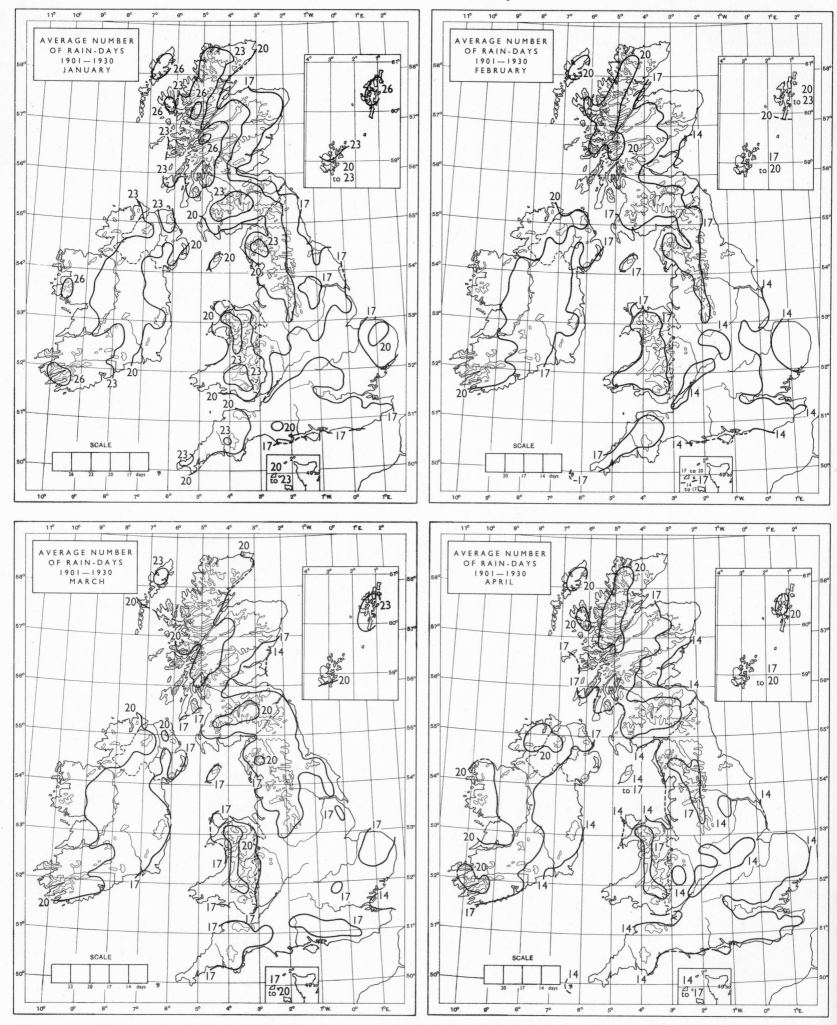

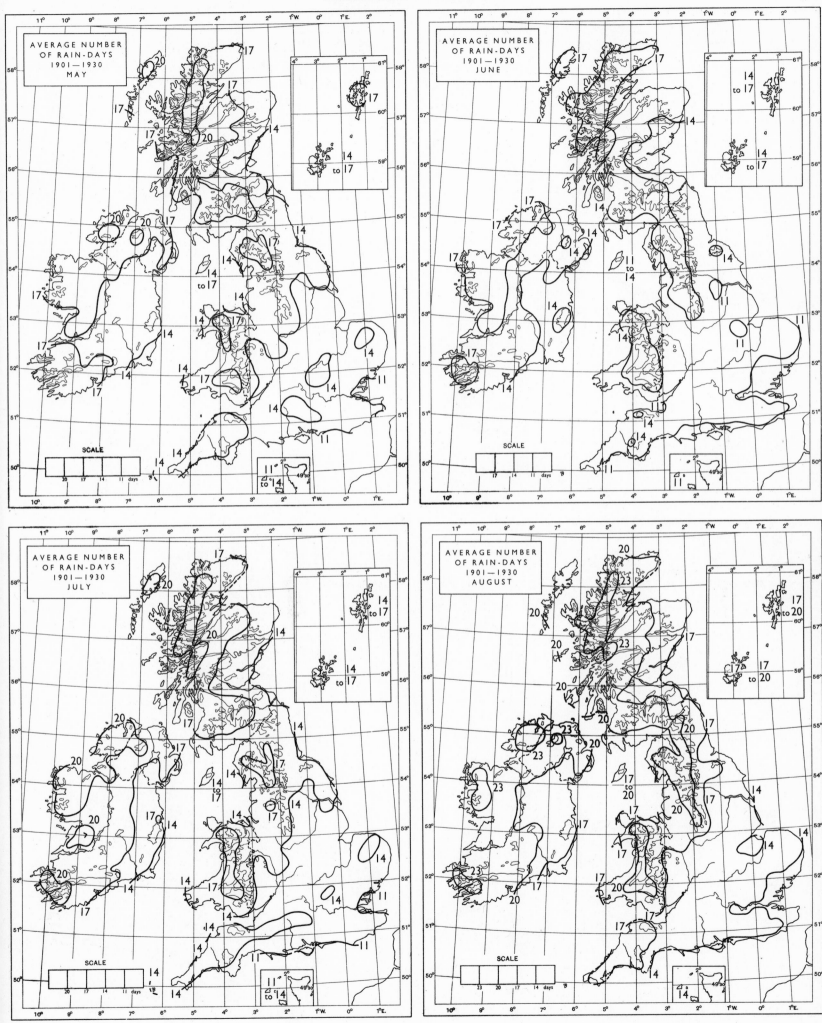

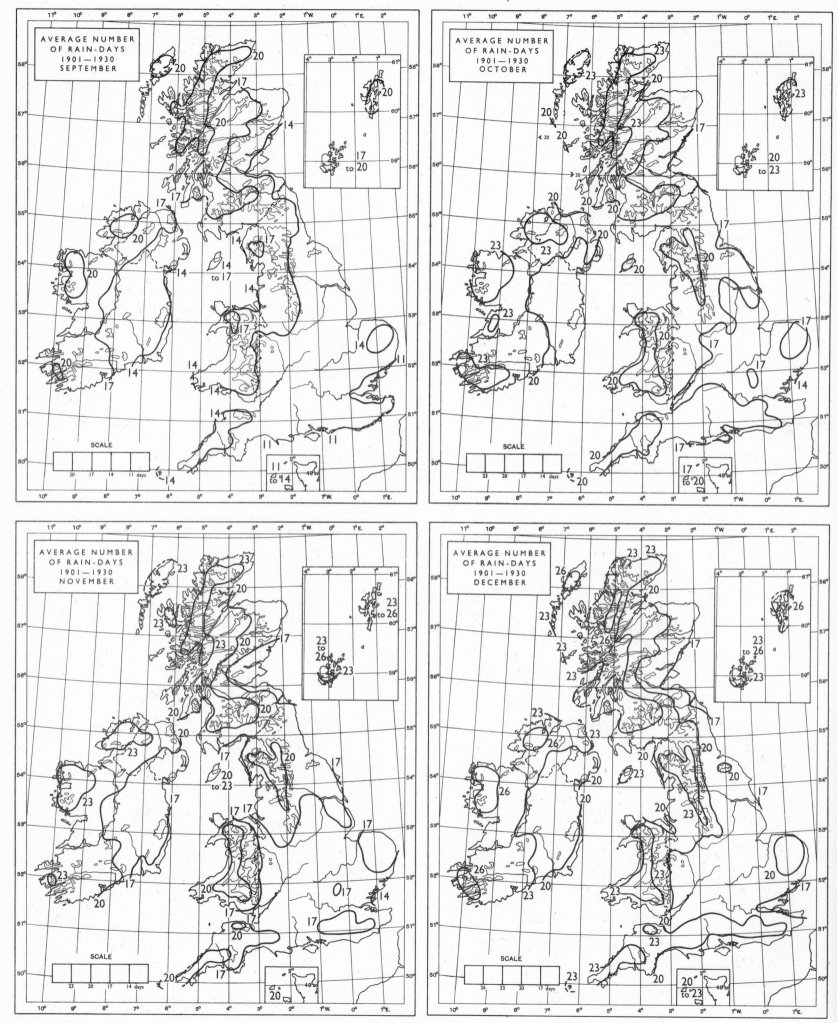

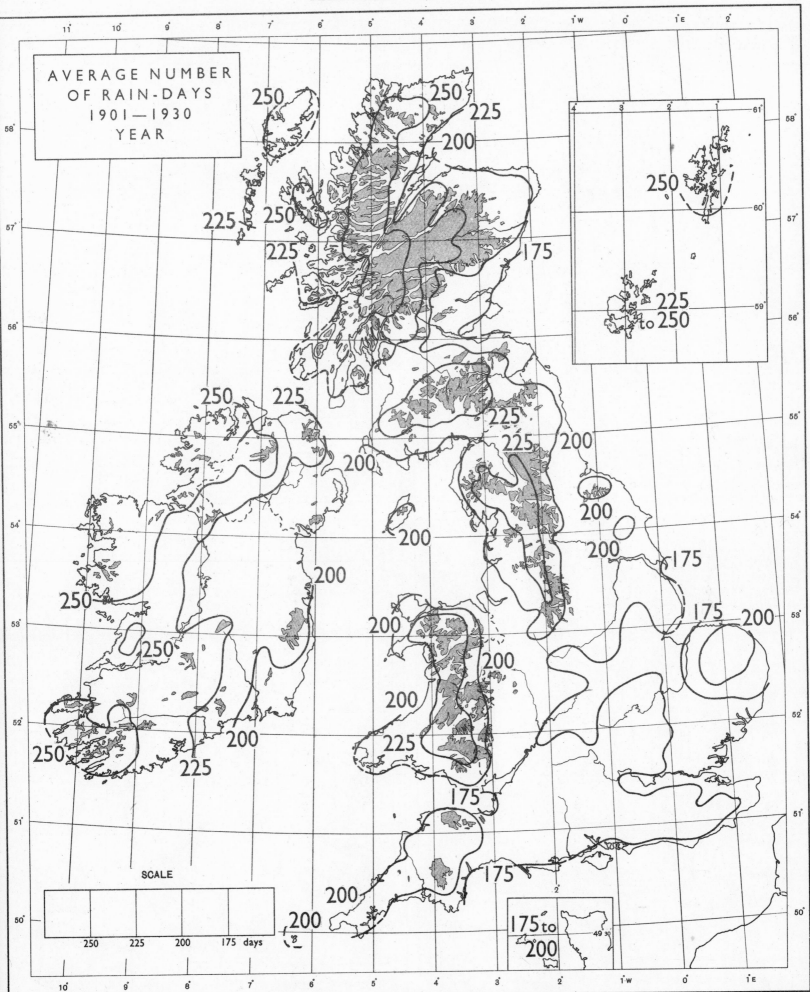

AVERAGE NUMBER
OF RAIN-DAYS
1901—1930
YEAR

250
250
225
200

250
225 to 250

225 250
225

175

250 225

225
225 200

200

200

200

200
175

175 200

250

250

200

200
200
225

225

200

175

175

250

200
200

175

SCALE

250   225   200   175 days

175 to
200

49 30

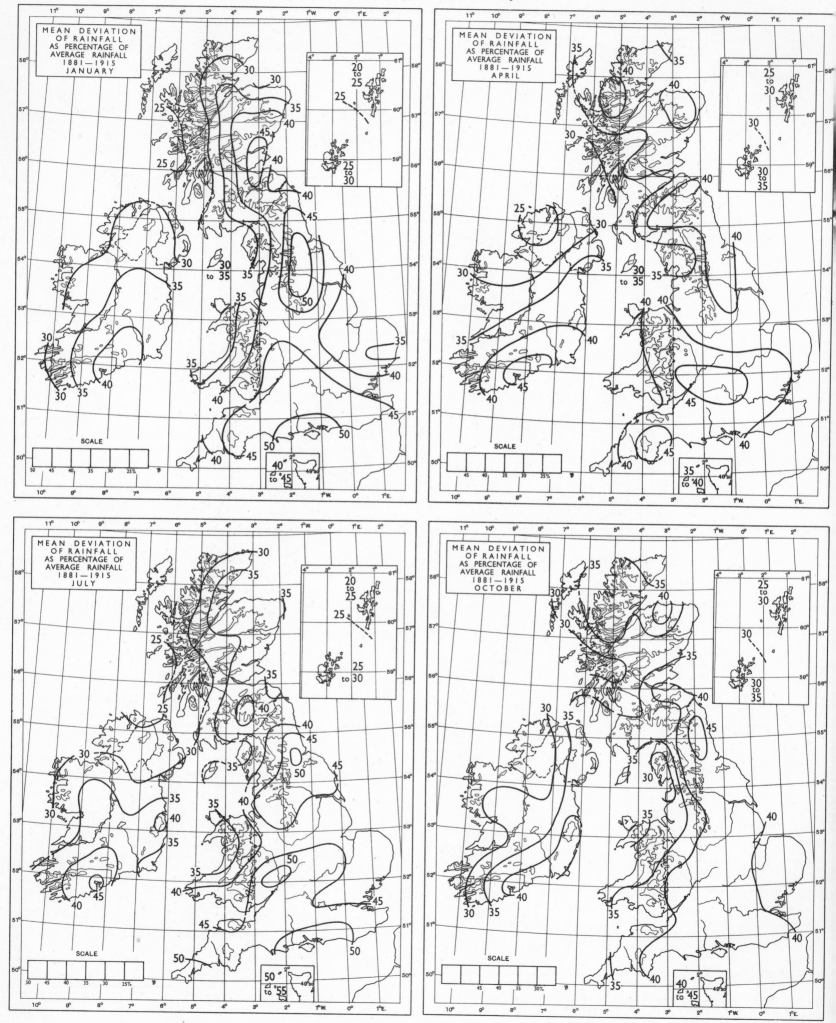

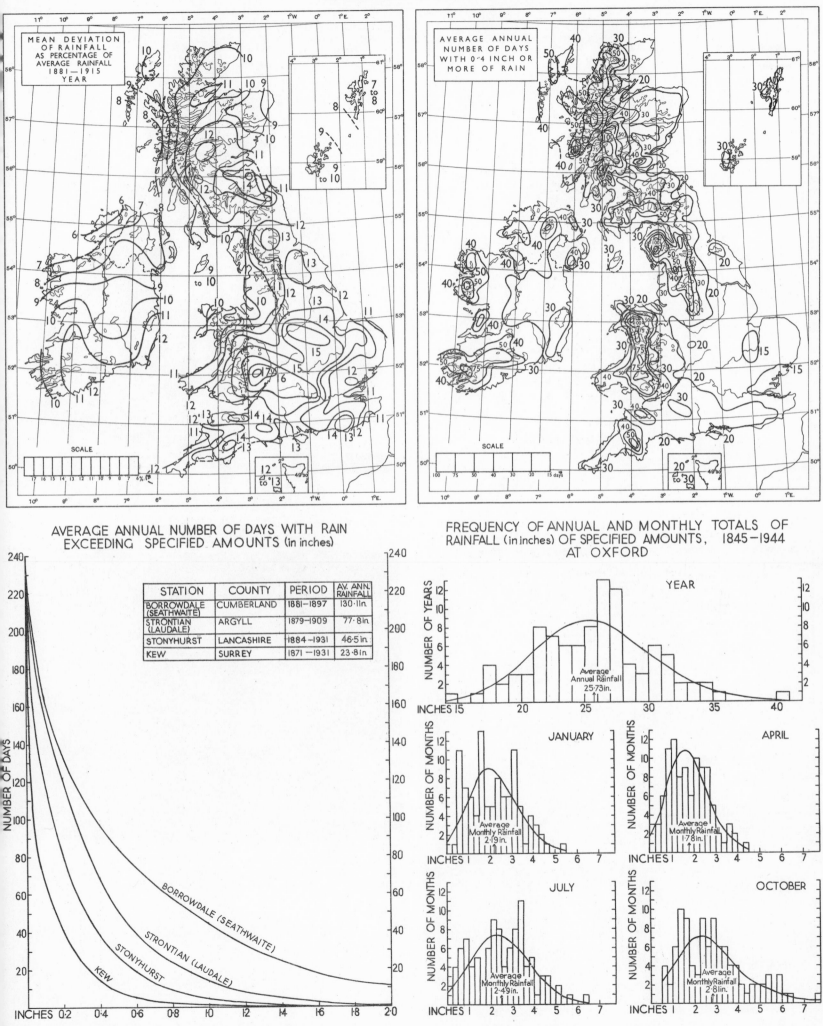

MEAN DEVIATION
OF RAINFALL
AS PERCENTAGE OF
AVERAGE RAINFALL
1881—1915
YEAR

SCALE

AVERAGE ANNUAL
NUMBER OF DAYS
WITH 0·4 INCH OR
MORE OF RAIN

SCALE

AVERAGE ANNUAL NUMBER OF DAYS WITH RAIN
EXCEEDING SPECIFIED AMOUNTS (in inches)

FREQUENCY OF ANNUAL AND MONTHLY TOTALS OF
RAINFALL (in inches) OF SPECIFIED AMOUNTS, 1845—1944
AT OXFORD

STATION	COUNTY	PERIOD	AV. ANN. RAINFALL
BORROWDALE (SEATHWAITE)	CUMBERLAND	1881—1897	130·11 in.
STRONTIAN (LAUDALE)	ARGYLL	1879—1909	77·8 in.
STONYHURST	LANCASHIRE	1884—1931	46·5 in.
KEW	SURREY	1871—1931	23·8 in.

NUMBER OF DAYS

BORROWDALE (SEATHWAITE)
STRONTIAN (LAUDALE)
STONYHURST
KEW

INCHES 0·2 0·4 0·6 0·8 1·0 1·2 1·4 1·6 1·8 2·0

YEAR
NUMBER OF YEARS
Average Annual Rainfall 25·73 in.
INCHES 15   20   25   30   35   40

JANUARY
NUMBER OF MONTHS
Average Monthly Rainfall 2·19 in.
INCHES 1 2 3 4 5 6 7

APRIL
NUMBER OF MONTHS
Average Monthly Rainfall 1·78 in.
INCHES 1 2 3 4 5 6 7

JULY
NUMBER OF MONTHS
Average Monthly Rainfall 2·49 in.
INCHES 1 2 3 4 5 6 7

OCTOBER
NUMBER OF MONTHS
Average Monthly Rainfall 2·81 in.
INCHES 1 2 3 4 5 6 7

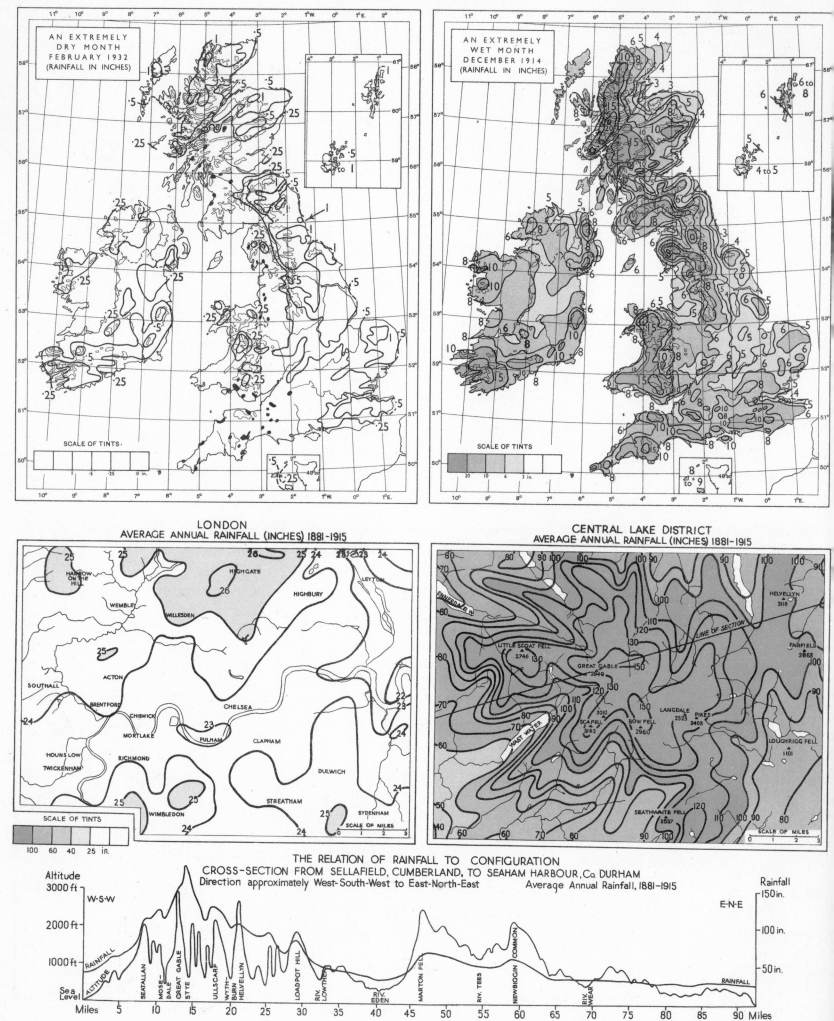

AN EXTREMELY
DRY MONTH
FEBRUARY 1932
(RAINFALL IN INCHES)

SCALE OF TINTS
1 · 5 · 25 · 0 in.

AN EXTREMELY
WET MONTH
DECEMBER 1914
(RAINFALL IN INCHES)

SCALE OF TINTS
20 10 6 3 in.

LONDON
AVERAGE ANNUAL RAINFALL (INCHES) 1881-1915

SCALE OF TINTS
100 60 40 25 in.

CENTRAL LAKE DISTRICT
AVERAGE ANNUAL RAINFALL (INCHES) 1881-1915

THE RELATION OF RAINFALL TO CONFIGURATION
CROSS-SECTION FROM SELLAFIELD, CUMBERLAND, TO SEAHAM HARBOUR, Cₒ DURHAM
Direction approximately West-South-West to East-North-East   Average Annual Rainfall, 1881-1915

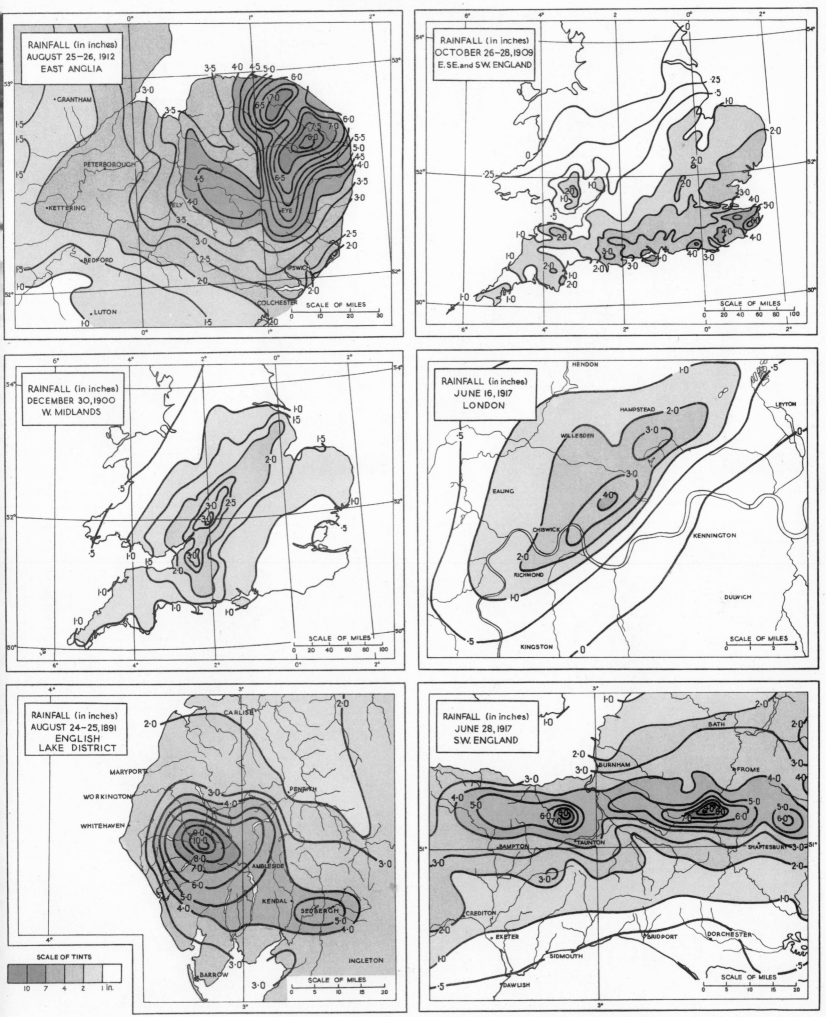

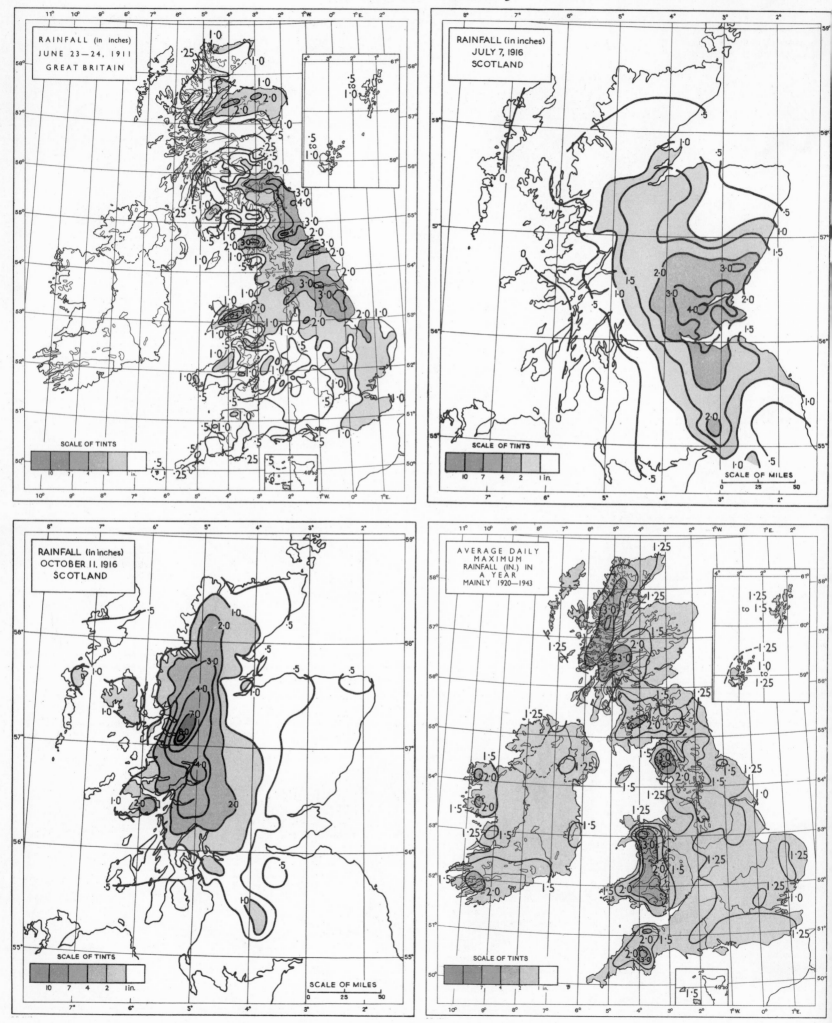

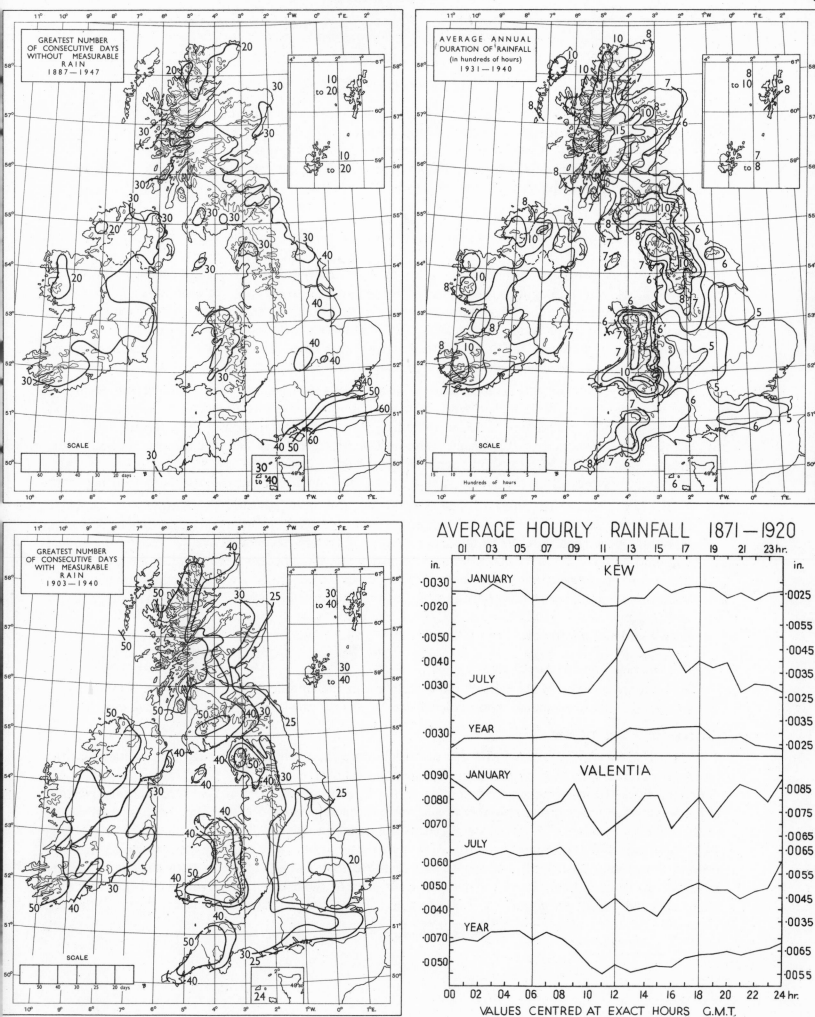

GREATEST NUMBER OF CONSECUTIVE DAYS WITHOUT MEASURABLE RAIN 1887—1947

SCALE
60 50 40 30 20 days

AVERAGE ANNUAL DURATION OF RAINFALL (in hundreds of hours) 1931—1940

SCALE
15 10 8 7 6 5
Hundreds of hours

GREATEST NUMBER OF CONSECUTIVE DAYS WITH MEASURABLE RAIN 1903—1940

SCALE
50 40 30 25 20 days

AVERAGE HOURLY RAINFALL 1871—1920

01 03 05 07 09 11 13 15 17 19 21 23 hr.

KEW
in.   in.
JANUARY
·0030   ·0025
·0020
·0055
JULY   ·0050   ·0045
·0040   ·0035
·0030   ·0025
YEAR
·0030   ·0035
·0025

VALENTIA
·0090   ·0085
JANUARY
·0080   ·0075
·0070   ·0065
JULY   ·0065
·0060   ·0055
·0050   ·0045
·0040   ·0035
YEAR   ·0070   ·0065
·0050   ·0055

00 02 04 06 08 10 12 14 16 18 20 22 24 hr.
VALUES CENTRED AT EXACT HOURS   G.M.T.

§5—SNOW

INTRODUCTION

The amounts of snow which fall over the British Isles are measured as rain ; thus, such amounts are included in the rainfall statistics in Section 4, and cannot be illustrated separately. This present section deals with two aspects of snowfall for which separate records are available—(a) the number of days when snow fell on low ground, *i.e.* ground up to 200 feet above mean sea level, and (b) the number of days when snow lay on the ground, and its depth.

(a) Days with Snow Falling on Low Ground

A day with snow falling is defined as one on which snow (or sleet) is observed at any time during the day.

The observer is instructed to note all occasions of snow or sleet, however slight, occurring during the civil day, that is from midnight to midnight. It is obvious that the number of such occasions recorded must depend on the possibility of a continuous watch being kept at the station. The maps are based on all available records of snow for the years 1912-1938 for about 150 stations used in the *Monthly weather report*. In reducing the statistics to a form which could be dealt with cartographically, the average frequency has been adjusted, where necessary, from two aspects :—

(i) At observatories and similar stations, where it was possible to maintain continuous record of the weather, the number of days with snow was found to be about 20 per cent. in excess of that reported at nearby stations. The latter stations formed the majority and their records have been adopted as the standard. The maps therefore can be regarded as defining the distribution of the average number of days with snow (or sleet), apart from occasions of a few flakes, especially at night. In order to cover all occasions the values throughout should be increased by about 20 per cent.

(ii) The average frequency of each station has also been adjusted to represent the probable frequency on low ground up to 200 feet above mean sea level. The records for stations at higher elevations have been reduced by one day for every 50 feet of elevation above 200 feet on the annual map and one day for every 300 feet on the monthly maps. This has been found to be a reasonable factor for the observations available[1]*. At heights exceeding 1,000 feet the values obtained by the addition of one day per 50 feet have been found to be too small. From a comparison of observations at Ben Nevis and Fort William in 1903-1904, the corrections to the annual totals at 0-200 feet have been estimated approximately as follows :—

Height in feet	1,000	1,500	2,000	2,500	3,000	3,500	4,000
Correction in days to value at 0-200 feet	+20	+35	+52	+70	+90	+115	+140

At high levels some of the falls of snow occurred in the summer months which were snow-free at low levels. No corrections applicable above 1,000 feet can be given for individual months.

(b) Days with Snow Lying

A day of snow lying is defined as a day on which more than half of the ground representative of the station is covered with snow at the morning observation hour.

Observations of this element were first taken in the British Isles in 1912, and in 1923 monthly averages of snow lying for a very limited number of stations over short periods, 1912-1920 or less, were published in the " Book of normals "[2]. The present maps are based on records of snow lying for the years 1912-1938 for about 150 stations used in the *Monthly weather report*, and are the first published maps to present the average distribution of snow lying in the British Isles. The data here used refer for the most part to comparatively low-level stations, a majority of them being at heights well below 500 feet, while only five are at an altitude of 1,000 feet or a little over, namely, Princetown, Buxton, Cantref,

---

* The superior figures refer to the bibliography on page 86.

Dalwhinnie and Braemar. The duration of snow-cover is influenced by many factors, among which may be mentioned—(i) monthly mean temperature; (ii) frequency of snowfall; (iii) quantity of snowfall; and (iv) the character of the station and its surroundings, such as its height, aspect and distance from hills[3]. In the British Isles snow lying is one of the most variable of meteorological elements and the averages were derived from very different values in individual years. In severe winters such as 1879 and 1881 and in more recent years 1940, 1941, 1942 and 1947, snow lay on the ground for long periods, whereas in some winter months the duration was almost negligible. For example, in February 1942 snow lying was reported on each day of the month over large areas in the east and north-east of Britain, whereas in February 1943 the majority of stations reported no single day of snow lying, the largest number of such days being six at both Braemar and Balmoral[4].

PLATES 1-3

MAPS OF AVERAGE NUMBER OF DAYS WITH SNOW FALLING ON LOW GROUND IN THE WINTER MONTHS AND THE YEAR, 1912-1938.—Although the adjustments mentioned above were made, the maps still show at some stations a large number of days with snow, due mainly to the effect of orography in giving rise to showers on many days when the lowlands were free. The greater frequency of instability snow showers on the east coast in the north-easterly type of pressure distribution is also well defined. The maps bring out very well the effect of latitude and of the proximity of the eastern districts to the colder continental air masses of winter. For example, compare (a) Scilly 3.5 days in the year with Stornoway 23.6 days and (b) Valentia 5.4 days with Felixstowe 12.9 days.

MAP SHOWING DEPTH OF SNOW IN SOUTHERN ENGLAND DURING THE SEVERE STORM OF CHRISTMAS 1927.—The map shows isopleths of the depth of level snow over southern England and south Wales during the storm of December 25-26, 1927. There were fairly large areas with a depth of more than 8 inches and it is probable that in a few places level snow was as much as 1 foot deep. The most notable features of the storm, however, were the deep drifts which were formed by the strong north-easterly wind which reached gale force in exposed places. The drifts were very great on Dartmoor, on Salisbury Plain and in parts of Hampshire; villages were isolated for several days, large numbers of sheep were buried and there was serious interruption of road and rail communication. Drifts up to 10 feet were widespread and occurred up to 20 feet locally on Dartmoor and Salisbury Plain. In some of the gullies on the moors above Harford, a village 2½ miles north of Ivybridge, the snow was said to be 60 feet deep. A detailed account of the storm has been given by Breton[5].

PLATES 4-8

MAPS OF AVERAGE NUMBER OF MORNINGS WITH SNOW LYING IN THE WINTER MONTHS AND THE YEAR, 1912-1938.—The annual map indicates how greatly the duration of snow-cover depends on altitude, the isopleths closely following the contour lines. Almost as important is the increase in the number of days from the south-west and west towards the east and north. For example, at Princetown (1,359 ft.) on Dartmoor, the number of days in the year was less than 20, compared with 68 at Braemar (1,111 ft.) in the Grampians. This difference is due largely to the influence of the Atlantic on the south-west and west regions and partly to the greater frequency of snow and, on the whole, the greater quantity of snowfall in the northern and eastern districts. The maps for December, January and February show the same general characteristics as the annual map. In March, however, the frequency of days with snow lying was lower than in the above months, particularly in parts of England. In November and April the number of days with snow lying was insignificant except in the Highlands of Scotland. For these months only the maps for Scotland are reproduced as insets in those for December and March respectively.

Although the summits of even the highest peaks in the British Isles are well below the permanent snow-line, there are certain hollows and gullies at high levels where snow accumulates in such large quantities during the winter that some of it remains unmelted during most summers. Of these the best known and the one possessing the best claim to be called permanent is the Great Corrie of Allt-a-Mhullin, north-east of the summit of Ben Nevis.

BIBLIOGRAPHY

[1] MANLEY, G.; Snowfall in the British Isles. *Met. Mag., London,* **75,** 1939, p. 41.

[2] London, Meteorological Office. The book of normals of meteorological elements for the British Isles for periods ending 1915. Section IVb, Frequency tables for hail, thunder, snow, snow lying and ground frost. London, 1923.

[3] MANLEY, G.; On the occurrence of snow-cover in Great Britain. *Quart. J.R. met. Soc., London,* **65,** 1939, p. 2.

[4] LEWIS, L. F.; Snow-cover in the British Isles in January and February of the severe winters of 1940, 1941 and 1942. *Quart. J.R. met. Soc., London,* **69,** 1943, pp. 215 and 286.

[5] BRETON, H. H.; The great blizzard of Christmas, 1927. Plymouth (Hoyten & Cole), 1928.

BONACINA, L. C. W.; Snowfall in the British Isles during the half-century 1876-1925. *Brit. Rainf., London,* **67,** 1927, p. 260.

BONACINA, L. C. W.; Snowfall in the British Isles during the decade 1926-1935. *Brit. Rainf., London,* **76,** 1936, p. 272.

DANSEY, R. P.; The glacial snows of Ben Nevis. *Symons's met. Mag., London,* **40,** 1905, p. 29.

JONES, J. R. G.; The spot in England and Wales where snow lies latest, with observations of snowfall on the Snowdonia range. *Brit. Rainf., London,* **49,** 1909, p. 46.

MANLEY, G.; Further climatological averages for the northern Pennines, with a note on topographical effects. *Quart. J.R. met. Soc., London,* **69,** 1943, p. 231.

MANLEY, G.; Topographical features and the climate of Britain. *Geogr. J., London,* **103,** 1944, p. 241.

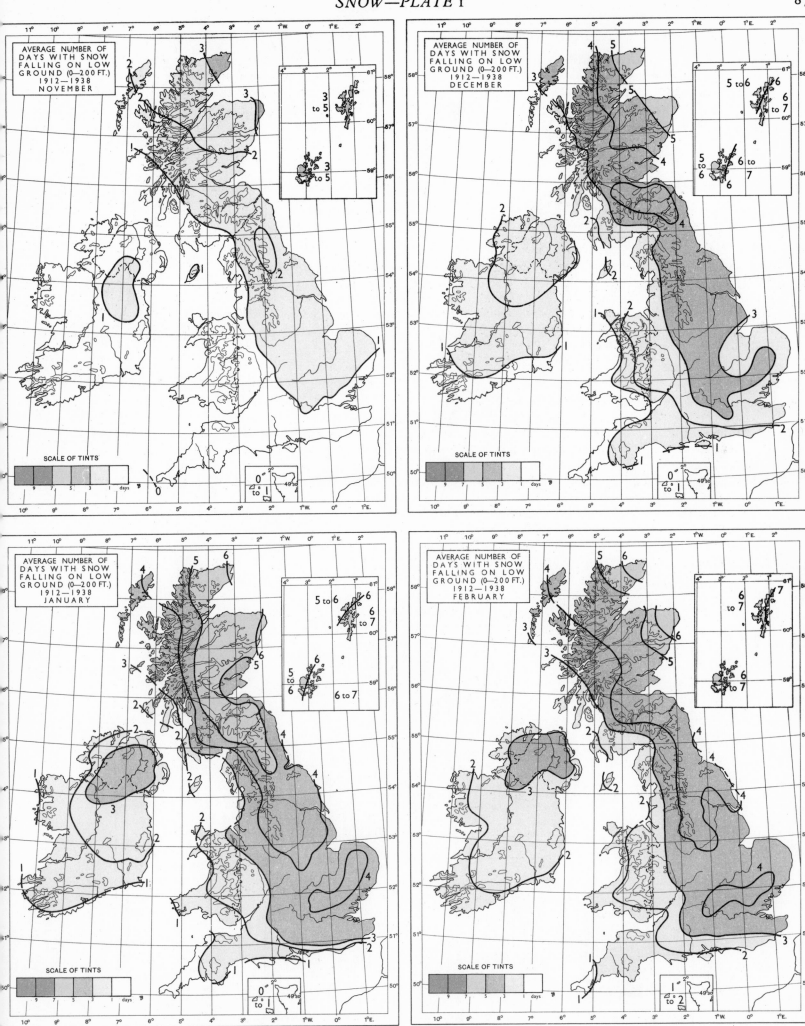

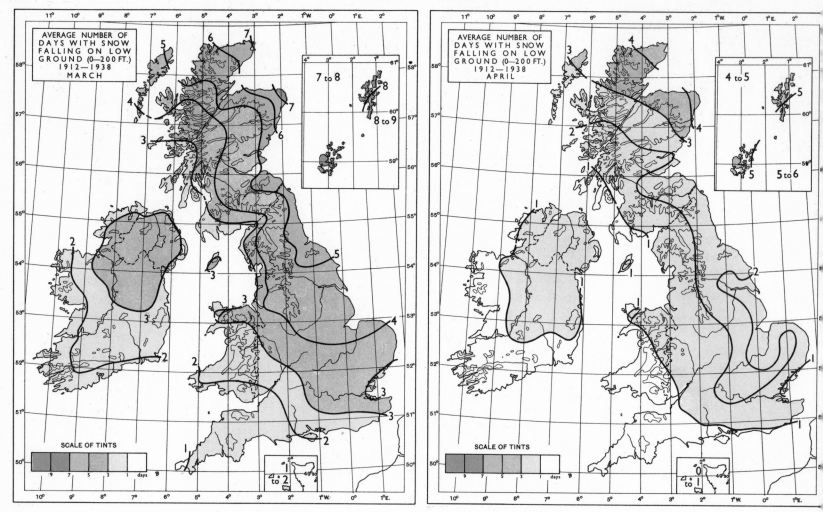

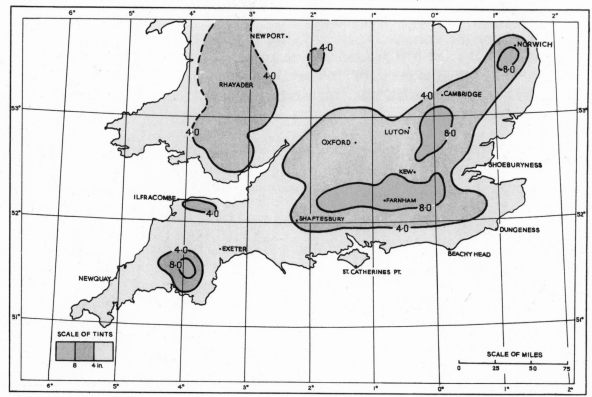

DEPTH (in inches) OF SNOW OVER SOUTHERN ENGLAND
DURING SEVERE STORM OF CHRISTMAS, 1927

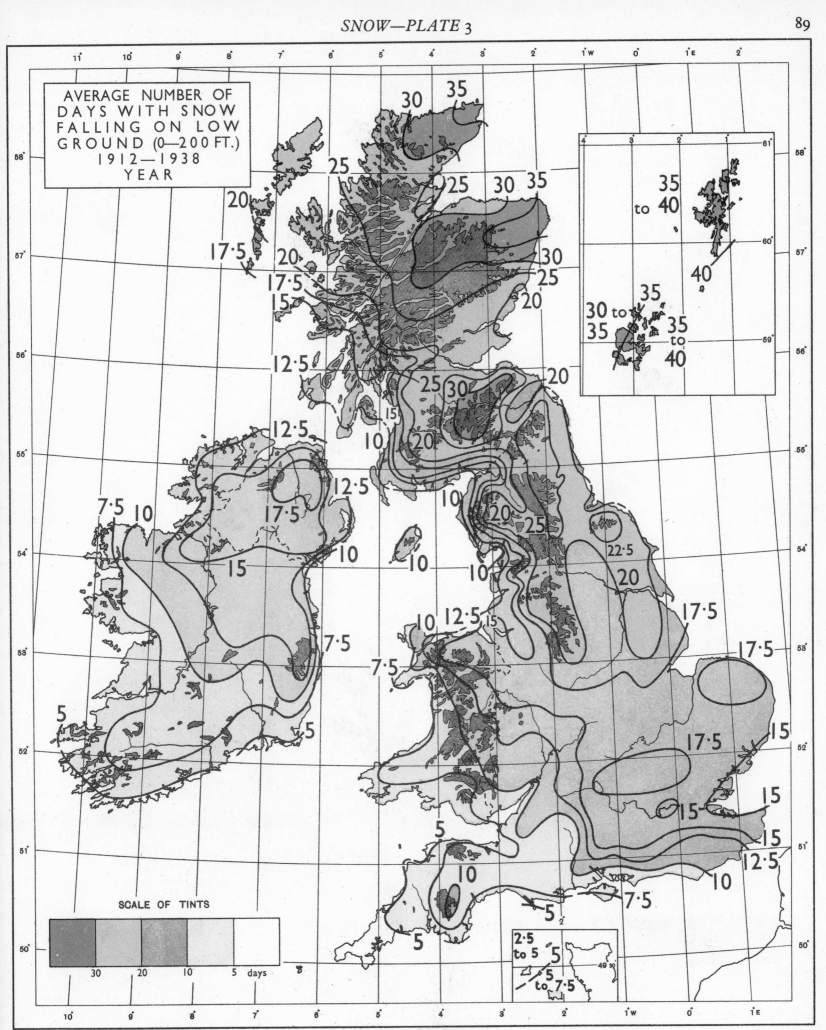

AVERAGE NUMBER OF DAYS WITH SNOW FALLING ON LOW GROUND (0—200 FT.) 1912—1938 YEAR

SCALE OF TINTS

30   20   10   5 days

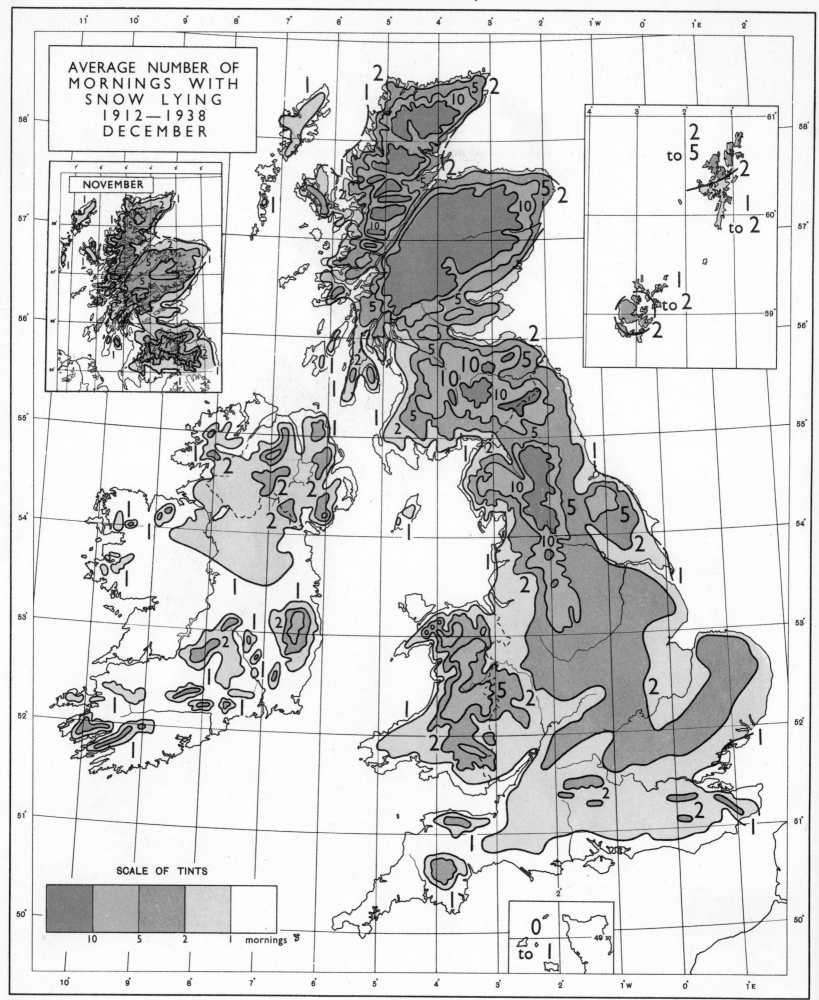

AVERAGE NUMBER OF
MORNINGS WITH
SNOW LYING
1912—1938
DECEMBER

NOVEMBER

SCALE OF TINTS

10   5   2   1   mornings

0
to 1

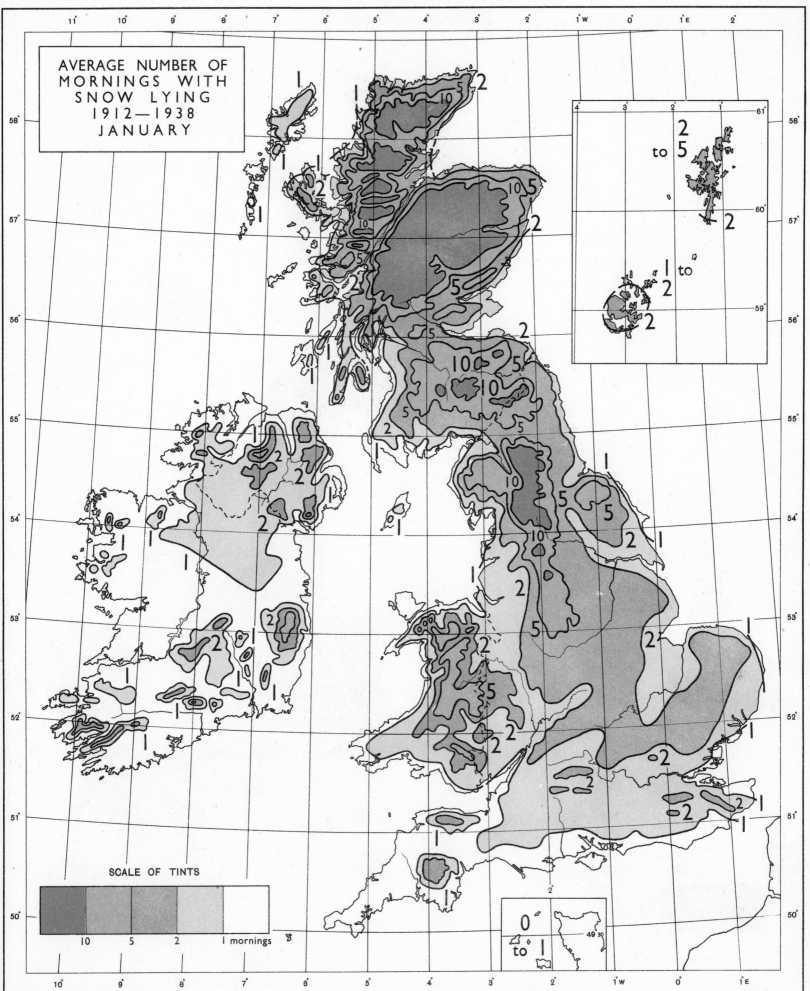

AVERAGE NUMBER OF
MORNINGS WITH
SNOW LYING
1912—1938
JANUARY

SCALE OF TINTS

10   5   2   1 mornings

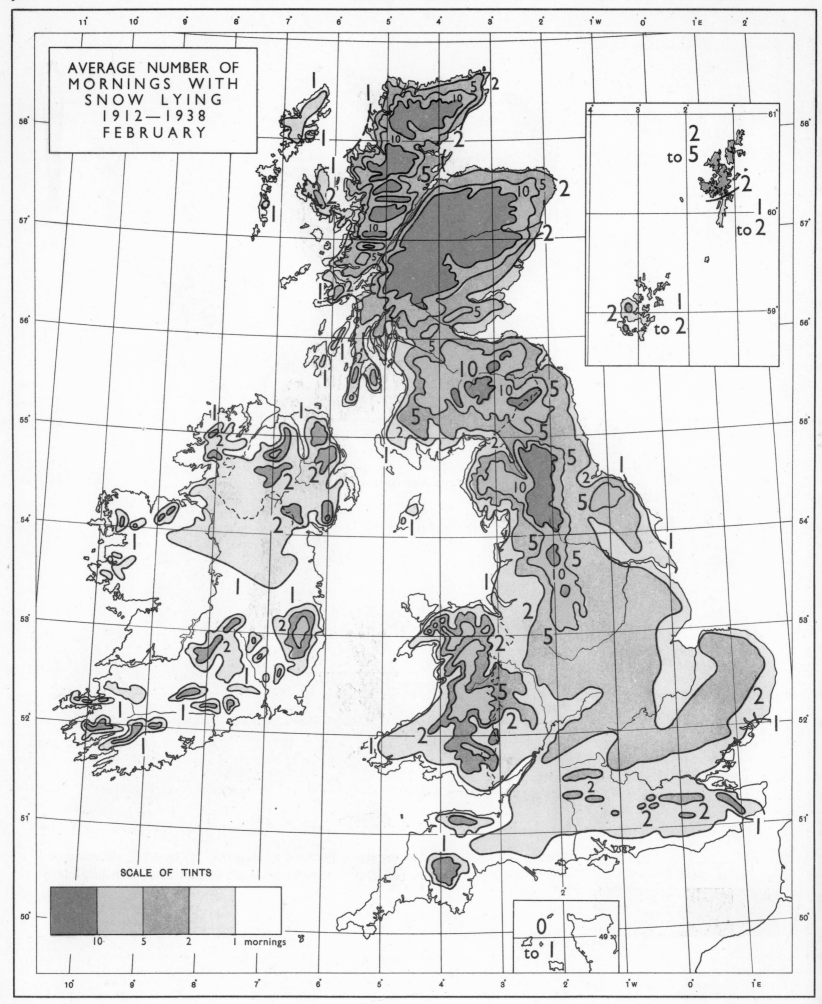

AVERAGE NUMBER OF
MORNINGS WITH
SNOW LYING
1912—1938
FEBRUARY

SCALE OF TINTS

10   5   2   1 mornings

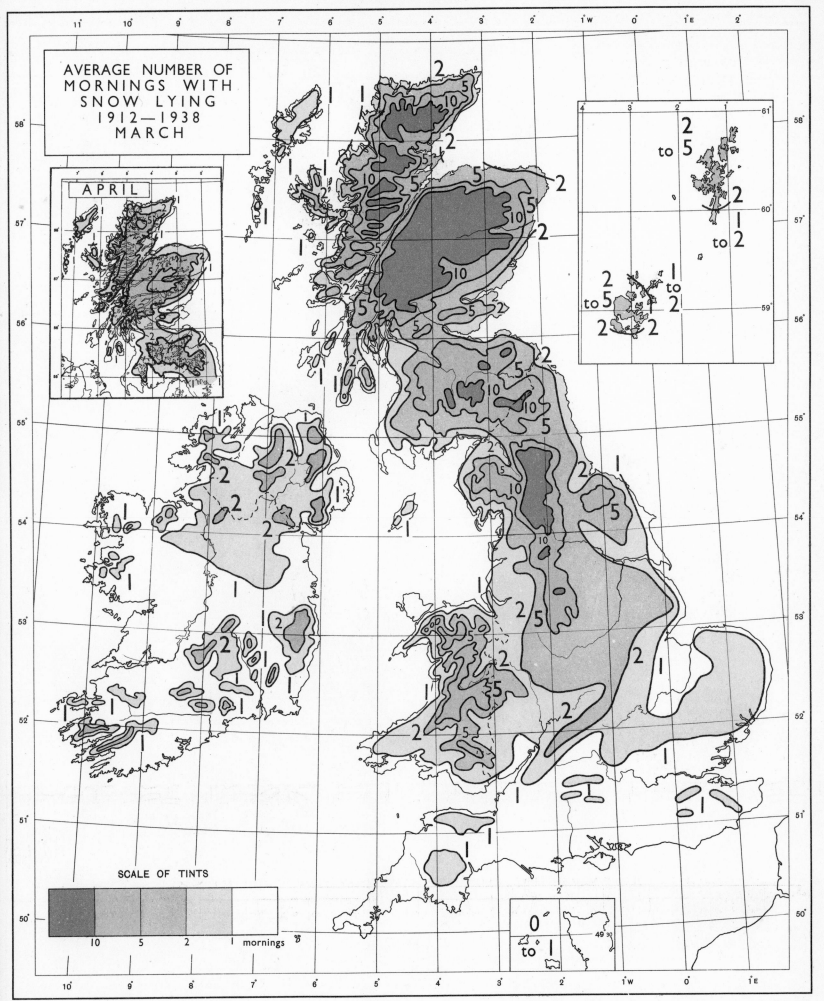

AVERAGE NUMBER OF
MORNINGS WITH
SNOW LYING
1912—1938
MARCH

APRIL

SCALE OF TINTS

10   5   2   1   mornings

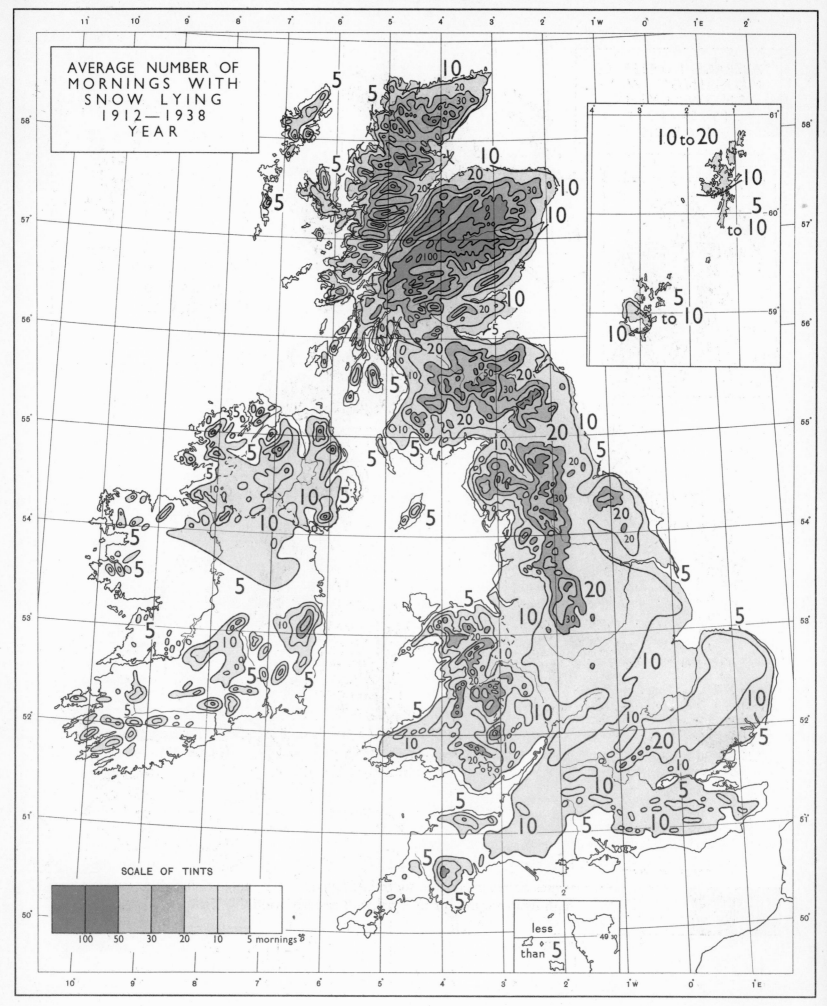

AVERAGE NUMBER OF
MORNINGS WITH
SNOW LYING
1912—1938
YEAR

10 to 20

5 to 10

SCALE OF TINTS

100   50   30   20   10   5 mornings

less than 5

§6—THUNDER

INTRODUCTION

" Thunder heard " is one of the observations which are recorded by weather observers, and summaries of days with thunder refer to the civil day, midnight to midnight. Observations of lightning seen without thunder heard are ignored in such summaries, and no distinction is made between overhead storms and those occasions when thunder is heard at a distance. Thunder is normally audible at distances up to about ten miles from the observer. Thus the statistics relate to those days on which there was a thunderstorm at or within about ten miles of the observing station at any time from midnight to midnight. The number of such occasions recorded at a station depended upon the ability of the observer to give continuous attention to the weather ; an occasion of thunder during the night, for instance, might have gone unrecorded.

Thunder is a very variable element in the British Isles. In Table I are given the highest and lowest numbers of days with thunder in a year at a few stations during the period 1901-1930.

TABLE I.—HIGHEST AND LOWEST ANNUAL NUMBER OF DAYS WITH THUNDER, 1901-1930

	Highest	Year	Lowest	Year
Deerness	14	1930	2	1904, 1914
Aberdeen	25	1924, 1930	2	1916, 1921
Yarmouth	25	1925	4	1907
Cambridge	26	1924	6	1919
Oxford ...	28	1925	7	1902, 1904
Kew	27	1924	9	1901, 1919, 1929
Stonyhurst	38	1912	6	1919
Portland Bill	20	1925	0	1920, 1922
Falmouth	11	1910	2	1925
Markree Castle	23	1912	3	1902
Valentia...	18	1912	1	1927

Previous maps showing the average frequency of days with thunder have been published by Marshall[1]*, using some 53 stations in the British Isles and by Bilham[2] using about 70 stations. The period covered in these maps was largely the 35 years 1881-1915, the authors using the figures given in the " Book of normals "[3], supplemented by values from additional stations.

The maps cannot give any indication of the severity or duration of thunderstorms. Two very prolonged storms in the London area, both notable for the brilliance and frequency of the lightning flashes, occurred on the nights of July 9-10, 1923 and July 14-15, 1945.

PLATES 1-3

MAPS OF AVERAGE NUMBER OF DAYS WITH THUNDER IN AUTUMN, WINTER, EACH OF THE MONTHS MARCH TO AUGUST, AND THE YEAR, 1901-1930.—The maps are based on records of thunder at 220 stations. In those cases where observations were only available for less than 15 years of the period, the values were revised by weighting with near-by stations. At a few stations data extending to a later period were adjusted to the selected 30-year period. In addition, as observations were first taken at a number of stations in 1911 or 1912, an annual map was constructed for the period 1911-1940 as a further guide to the general distribution. By these means, and with a knowledge of the procedure at individual stations, it was possible to arrive at the most likely distribution of thunderstorms over the British Isles during the period 1901-1930.

The winter chart on Plate 1 shows the relatively high frequency of winter thunderstorms in the north-west and west of the British Isles. This subject has been discussed by Newnham[4].

---

* The superior figures refer to the bibliography on page 96.

BIBLIOGRAPHY

[1] MARSHALL, W. A. L.; The mean frequency of thunder over the British Isles and surrounding areas. *Quart. J.R. met. Soc., London,* **60,** 1934, p. 413.

[2] BILHAM, E. G.; The climate of the British Isles. London (Macmillan), 1938.

[3] London, Meteorological Office. The book of normals of meteorological elements for the British Isles for periods ending 1915. Section IVb, Frequency tables for hail, thunder, snow, snow lying and ground frost. London, 1923.

[4] NEWNHAM, E. V.; On the formation of thunderstorms over the British Isles in winter. *Prof. notes met. Off., London,* **3,** No. 29, 1922.

DOUGLAS, C. K. M.; A note on frontal thunderstorms. *Met. Mag., London,* **69,** 1934, p. 206.

Huddersfield, Thunderstorm Census Organization. British thunderstorms. Annual summaries, 1925-1947.

MARRIOTT, W.; Second report of the Thunderstorm Committee. Distribution of thunderstorms over England and Wales, 1871-1887. *Quart. J.R. met. Soc., London,* **16,** 1890, p. 1.

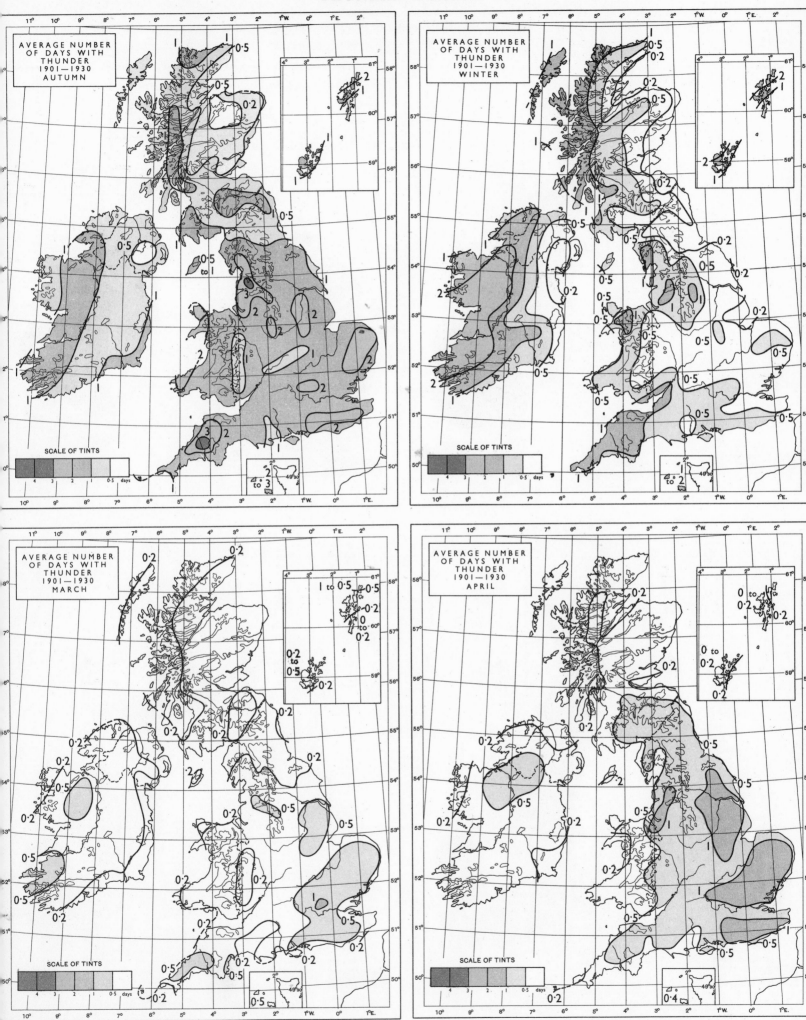

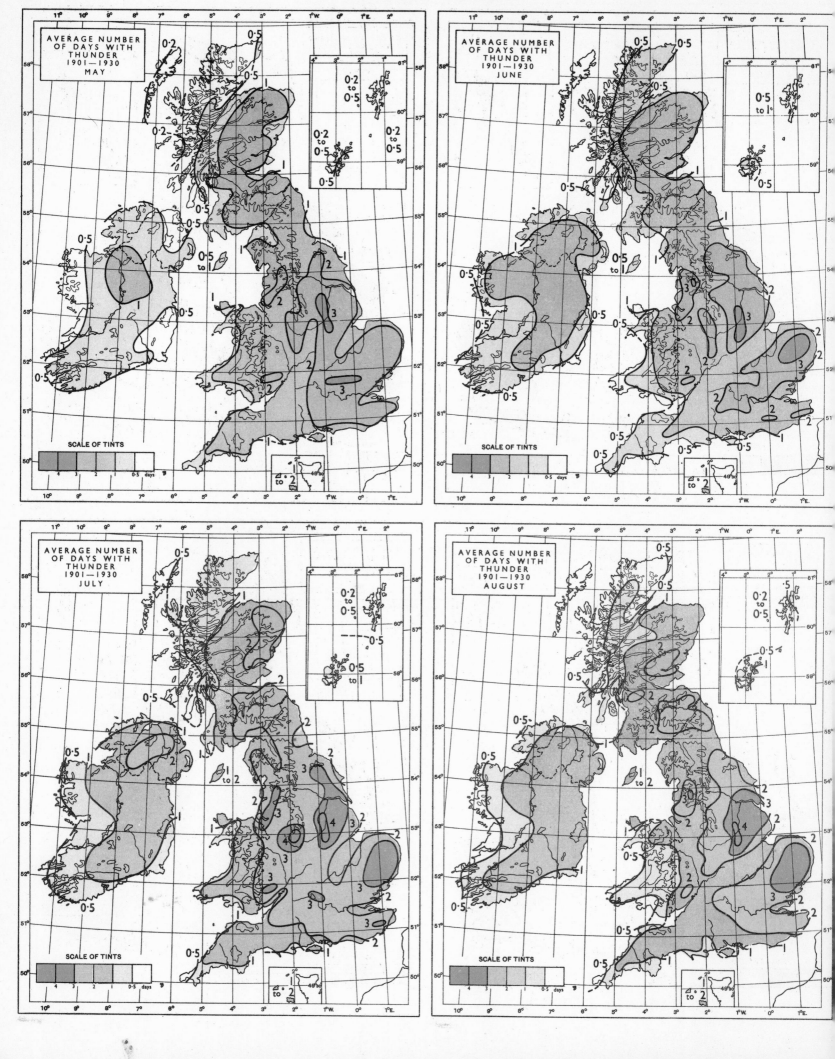

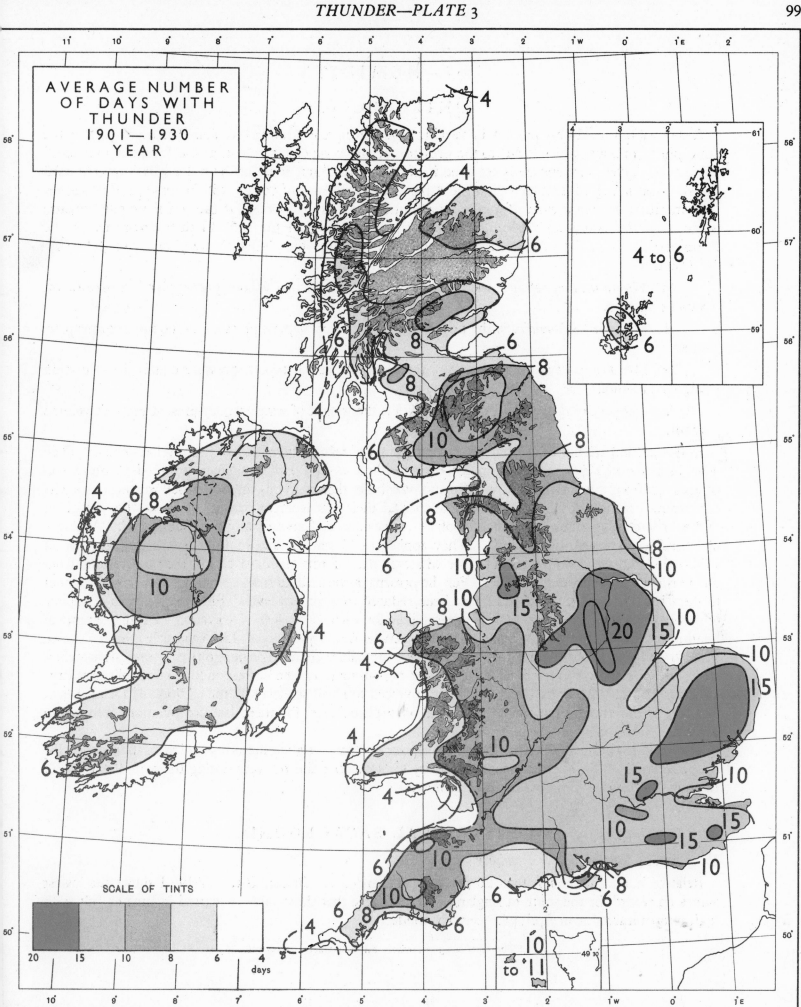

AVERAGE NUMBER
OF DAYS WITH
THUNDER
1901—1930
YEAR

4 to 6

SCALE OF TINTS

20   15   10   8   6   4
days

10
to 11

§7—HUMIDITY

INTRODUCTION

Water vapour is always present in varying amounts in the atmosphere, and that small part of the atmospheric pressure which is due to the presence of water vapour is known as the " vapour pressure."

If air at a given temperature is confined in contact with water, some of the water will evaporate until the air is saturated with water vapour, and the vapour pressure of the air will increase until it reaches the saturation vapour pressure for that temperature. Air is unsaturated if the actual vapour pressure is less than the saturation vapour pressure at the temperature of the air. In such circumstances the hygrometric state of the air may be expressed in various ways, some of which are given by the following definitions :—

(a) The *saturation deficit* is the difference between the actual vapour pressure and the saturation vapour pressure.

(b) The *relative humidity* is the percentage of the actual vapour pressure to the saturation vapour pressure.

(c) The *dew point* is the temperature for which the actual vapour pressure equals the saturation vapour pressure.

(d) The *vapour density* or *absolute humidity* is the weight of water vapour present per unit volume of air.

In this section are published maps of vapour pressure, relative humidity and saturation deficit. They have been derived from observations of dry-bulb and wet-bulb thermometers exposed in Stevenson screens or from photographic dry-bulb and wet-bulb thermographs in north-wall screens. Details concerning the care of wet-bulb thermometers and their management during frosty weather are given in the " Meteorological observer's handbook "[1]*. The data used have already been published in "Averages of humidity for the British Isles "[2]. They applied to 65 stations and to 13h. for the standard period 1921-1935, and were simple averages for whatever part of this standard period the observations from any particular station were available. For the present purpose these simple averages have been weighted to the whole period 1921-1935, and have been reduced to mean sea level. First the averages of vapour pressure were so reduced by adding one millibar for each 2,000 feet of elevation—a rough empirical relationship which was derived from graphs of average vapour pressure at 13h. against height, for twelve English and five Scottish inland stations. Then the values of relative humidity and saturation deficit were based on these corrected values of vapour pressure and on the corresponding values of mean dry-bulb temperature, the latter being themselves reduced to mean sea level by the addition of 1°F. for each 300 feet of elevation. The values of saturation pressure used for these last computations were those given in " Hygrometric tables "[3].

The section also includes some graphs of vapour pressure, relative humidity and saturation deficit for four observatories for alternate months January to November and the year during the period 1901-1930, to show the diurnal variation of these elements.

HISTORICAL BACKGROUND

Exceptionally Low Values of Humidity

Relative humidities of less than 20 per cent. are rare in the British Isles. Table I shows the lowest values on record for the south of England. It is notable that these values occurred in June or July with high temperatures, or in April with easterly winds.

---

* The superior figures refer to the bibliography on page 103.

TABLE I.—LOW VALUES OF RELATIVE HUMIDITY

Relative Humidity	Station	Date	Time	Dry-bulb temperature
%				°F.
10	Kew	April 15, 1942	15h. 15m.	57
13	Kew	June 3, 1939	18h.	70
15	Cardington	April 1, 1931	12h.	47
17	Kew			46
15	S. Farnborough	July 10, 1934	16h.	82
16	Kew		13h.	78
19	Kew	July 11, 1921	14h.	86

PLATES 1-10

MAPS OF AVERAGE MONTHLY AND ANNUAL MEANS OF VAPOUR PRESSURE, RELATIVE HUMIDITY AND SATURATION DEFICIT AT 13H., 1921-1935.—The relatively small number of stations for which data were available meant that only the broadest features of the distribution of these elements could be shown by isopleths. Local peculiarities of climate necessitated recourse to a certain amount of smoothing.

For the year, the general distribution of *vapour pressure* shows values which diminish from south-south-west to north-north-east combined with distance from the sea. The range extends from 12·4mb. at Scilly to 9·0mb. or slightly less on the highest Scottish mountains. A similar distribution is shown in individual months, with a range for June to October somewhat larger than the annual one.

In the maps of *relative humidity* the decrease of vapour pressure from south-south-west to north-north-east is more than compensated by the fall of temperature in the same direction (see Section 3—Temperature), and the decrease of vapour pressure with distance from the sea is reinforced by a corresponding rise of temperature. Distance from the sea, therefore, becomes the dominant factor in the annual distribution of relative humidity, and also in most of the individual months, the lowest humidities being inland. In January and December this effect is relatively slight and the total variation small.

The maps of relative humidity may be used to give an approximation to the average relative humidity at any place for its own level, by using the corrections given in Table II.

TABLE II.—CORRECTIONS TO RELATIVE HUMIDITY AT MEAN SEA LEVEL AT 13H. FOR OBTAINING RELATIVE HUMIDITY AT 1,000 FEET

(for any other height h multiply correction by $h/1,000$)

Temperature at station.	Relative Humidity per cent. at M.S.L.				
	90	80	70	60	50
°F.			*Per cent.*		
30	+4·2	+2·7	+1·2	—0·2	—1·6
40	+6·4	+5·0	+3·7	+2·3	+0·9
50	+7·8	+6·4	+5·1	+3·8	+2·5
60	+8·4	+7·2	+5·9	+4·7	+3·4
70	+8·8	+7·6	+6·4	+5·2	+4·0
80	+8·8	+7·7	+6·6	+5·4	+4·3

Saturation deficit at mean sea level is equal to $e(100-H)/100$ where e is the vapour pressure and H the relative humidity, both reduced to mean sea level. Of the component factors $(100-H)$ is by far the most important, and the general distribution of saturation deficit is roughly the inverse to that of relative humidity. But the deficit for a given value of $100-H$ is greater at high than at low temperatures because the saturation vapour pressure increases with temperature. It is for this reason that the area of high deficit in Scotland is less pronounced than the corresponding area in England, where temperature is higher, while the minima of relative humidity in the two countries are not very different.

The maps of saturation deficit can be used to give an approximation to the average saturation deficit for any place for its own level, by using the corrections given in Table III.

TABLE III.—CORRECTIONS IN MILLIBARS TO SATURATION DEFICIT AT MEAN SEA LEVEL AT
13H. FOR OBTAINING SATURATION DEFICIT AT HEIGHT h

Temperature at station	Height h in feet				
	200	400	600	800	1,000
°F.			*Millibars*		
30	—0·06	—0·12	—0·18	—0·24	—0·32
40	—0·11	—0·24	—0·37	—0·51	—0·65
50	—0·21	—0·43	—0·64	—0·85	—1·11
60	—0·32	—0·65	—1·00	—1·36	—1·71
70	—0·48	—0·97	—1·46	—1·97	—2·50
80	—0·67	—1·36	—2·05	—2·77	—3·50

GRAPHS OF HOURLY VALUES OF TEMPERATURE, RELATIVE HUMIDITY AND SATURATION DEFICIT FOR A WARM DRY DAY AND A WARM DAMP DAY AT KEW.—The first set of graphs under the title " Graphs of Extreme Humidity," is for a day in July when relative humidity was well below the average for July, the variation being from about 73 per cent. to 16 per cent. compared with the average range (see Plate 12) from about 88 per cent. to 59 per cent.   The highest value of the saturation deficit (28mb.), and the lowest humidity (16 per cent.) were at about 13h. G.M.T., but the maximum temperature of 80°F. was not reached until nearly 16h. G.M.T.

The second set of graphs is for a day with much cloud, intermittent rain, and a severe thunderstorm in the afternoon, following a sunny interval.   The storm brought no relief from the rather sultry conditions that preceded it, as saturation deficit was lower and relative humidity higher after the storm than at any time before it.

As examples of the high degree of discomfort that can be experienced as a result of excessive heat and humidity in England, mention may be made of August 29, 1930, when the dry-bulb reached 89·1°F. with wet-bulb 75·7°F., and August 19, 1932, when the corresponding figures were 91·6°F. and 75·4°F., in both cases at Kew.

PLATES 11 AND 12

GRAPHS OF AVERAGE HOURLY VAPOUR PRESSURE, SATURATION DEFICIT AND RELATIVE HUMIDITY AT STATION LEVEL, 1901-1930.—Graphs of the three elements for four observatories for alternate months from January to November and for the year are based on photographic dry-bulb and wet-bulb thermographs in north-wall screens.

For *vapour pressure* there is a minimum in the early morning and a maximum in the afternoon or evening.   Neither extreme is very sharply defined.   This diurnal range, rather small in all seasons, is greater in summer than in winter.   It is doubtless due largely to the diurnal range of temperature.   There is normally a temporary condensation of some of the water vapour as dew or hoar frost at night.   The increase in the average speed of the wind during the day assists re-evaporation.   On the coast, land and sea breezes will generally tend to give a similar diurnal variation.   On the other hand, the diurnal variation of temperature within the soil is less than that on the ground.   Consequently, in the exchange of water-vapour between the soil and the air above it, the soil may gain more than it loses during the day and conversely at night.   This would tend to diminish the diurnal variation due to the other causes referred to above.

Saturation deficit will be seen to have a much larger diurnal range, which is closely connected with the diurnal range of temperature, and is greatest in summer.   The small decrease of deficit in the afternoon, which would result from the greater vapour pressure at that time, is negligible compared with the large increase due to the greatly increased saturation pressure at the higher temperature.

The graphs of *relative humidity* are roughly the reverse of those for saturation deficit with temperature again the dominating factor.

BIBLIOGRAPHY

[1] London, Meteorological Office. Meteorological observer's handbook. London, 1942.

[2] London, Meteorological Office. Averages of humidity for the British Isles. London, 1938.

[3] London, Meteorological Office. Hygrometric tables. London, 1940.

DIGHT, F. H.; An analysis of warm spells in London from 1903-1933 with special reference to the prevailing conditions of humidity. *Met. Mag., London*, **69,** 1934, p. 109.

DRUMMOND, A. J.; Abnormally dry air at Kew Observatory. *Quart. J.R. met. Soc., London*, **68,** 1942, p. 293.

HAWKE, E. L.; The incidence of extremely low relative humidity in southern England. *Quart. J.R. met. Soc., London*, **70,** 1944, p. 274.

PICK, W. H.; A noteworthy spell of dry air over England. *Met. Mag., London*, **66,** 1931, p. 80.

READ, R. S.; Exceptionally dry air. *Quart. J.R. met. Soc., London*, **68,** 1942, p. 294.

STACEY, W. F.; Distribution of relative humidity in England and Wales. *Quart. J.R. met. Soc., London*, **41,** 1915, p. 45.

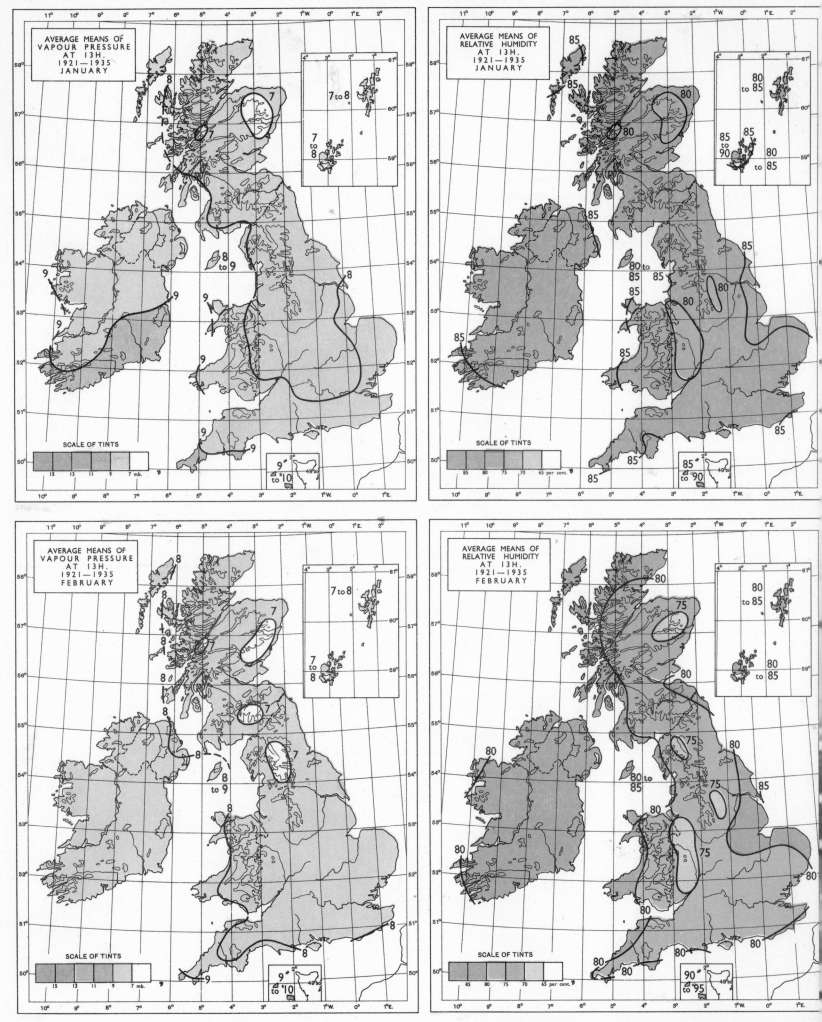

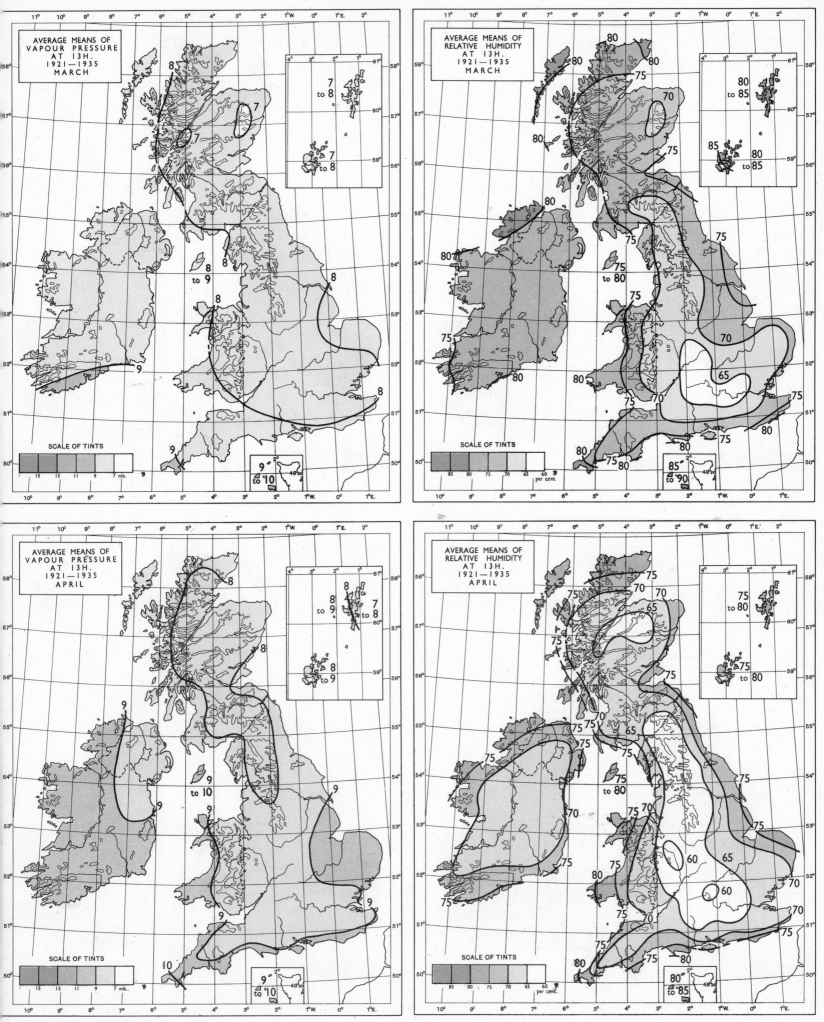

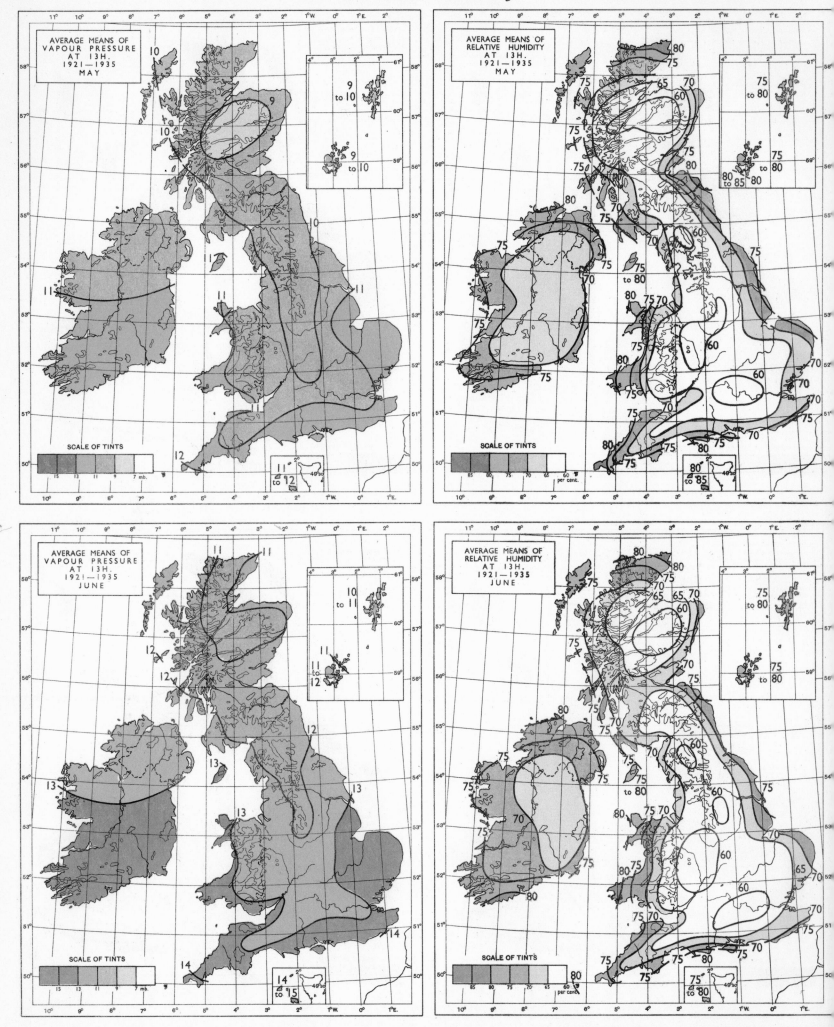

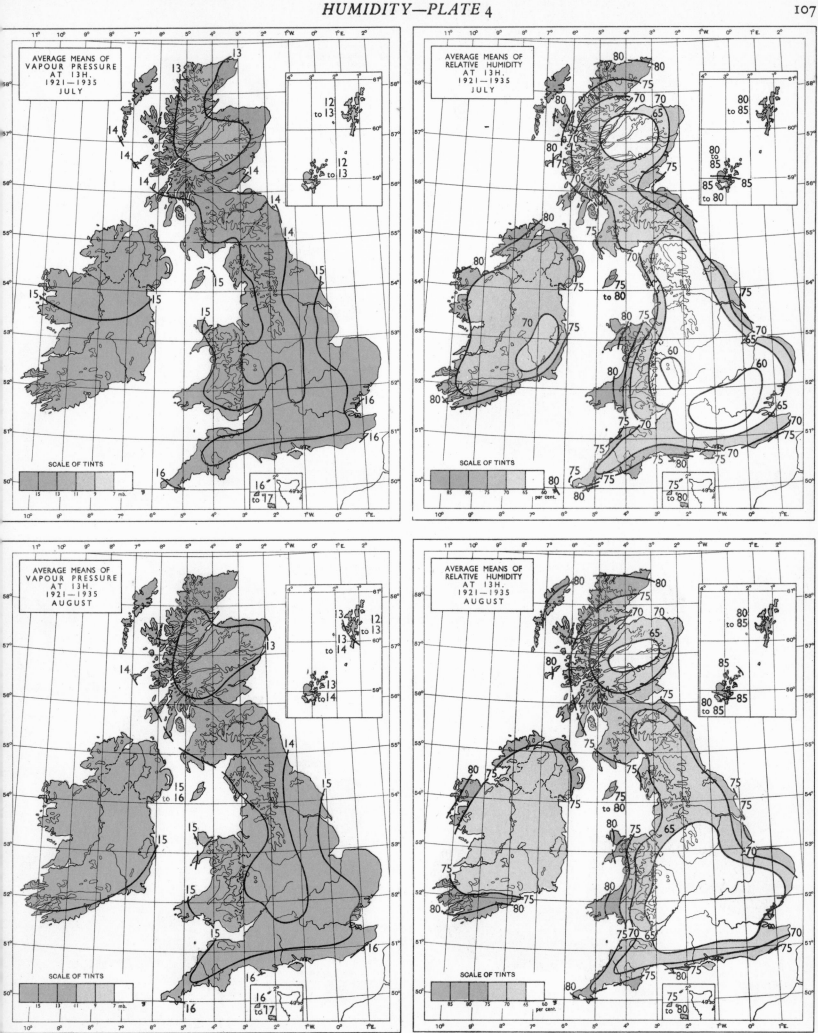

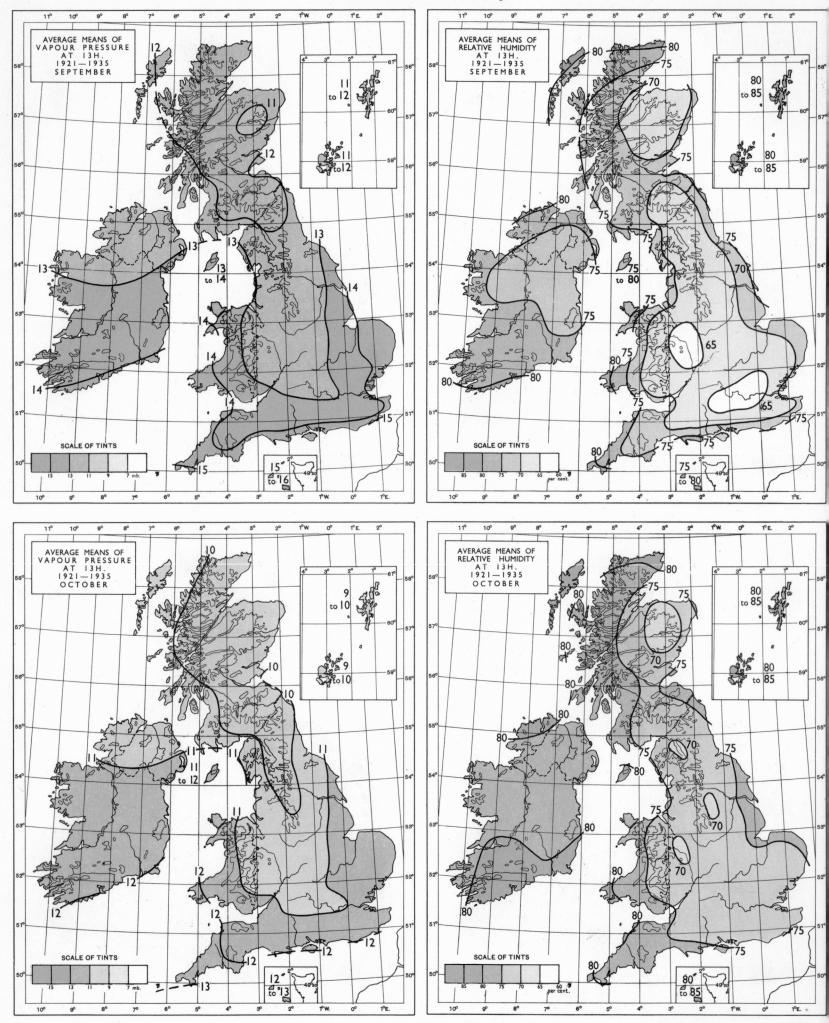

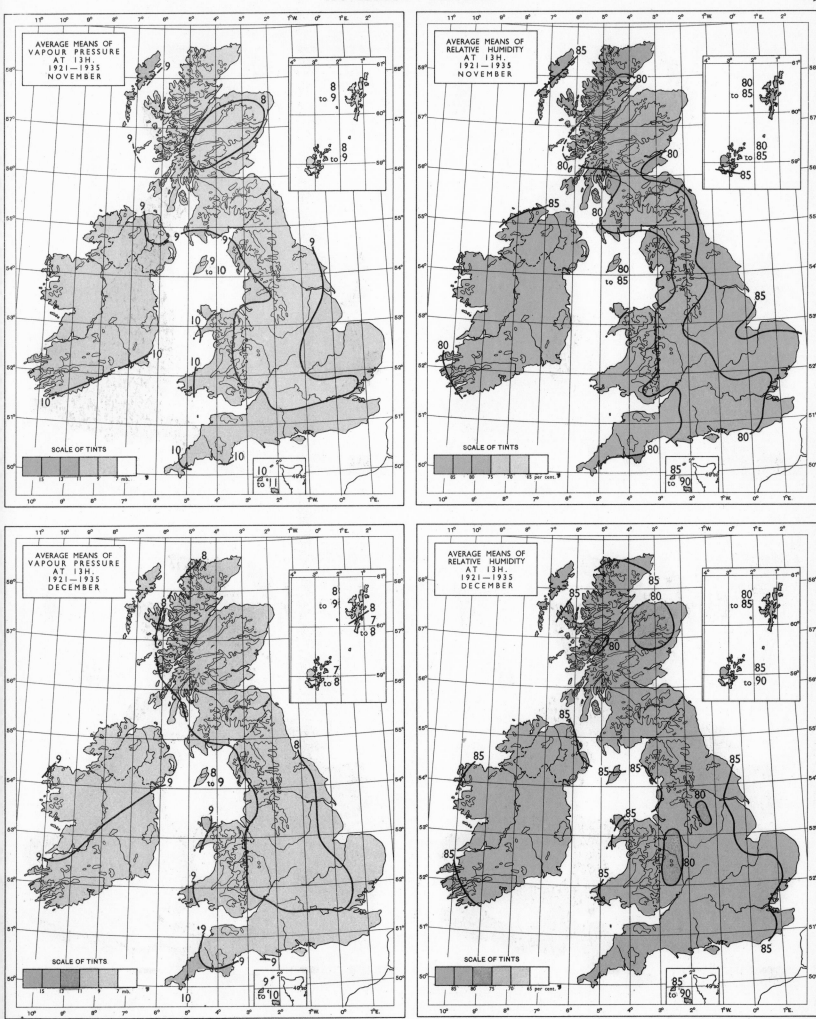

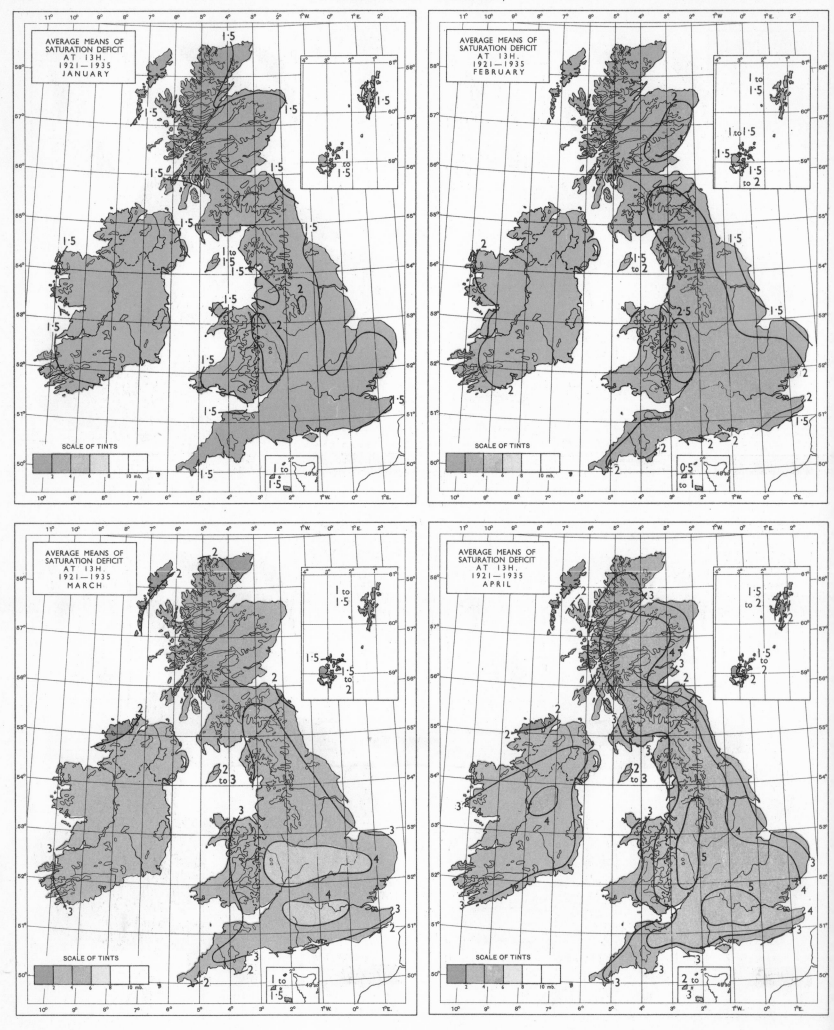

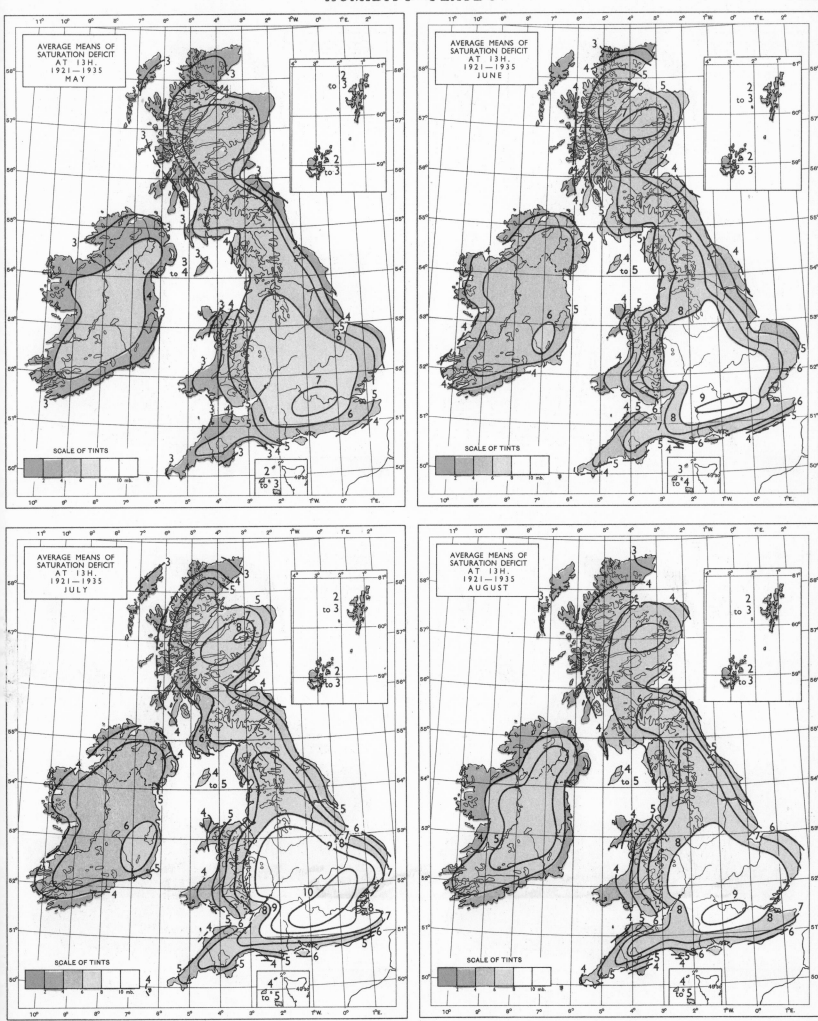

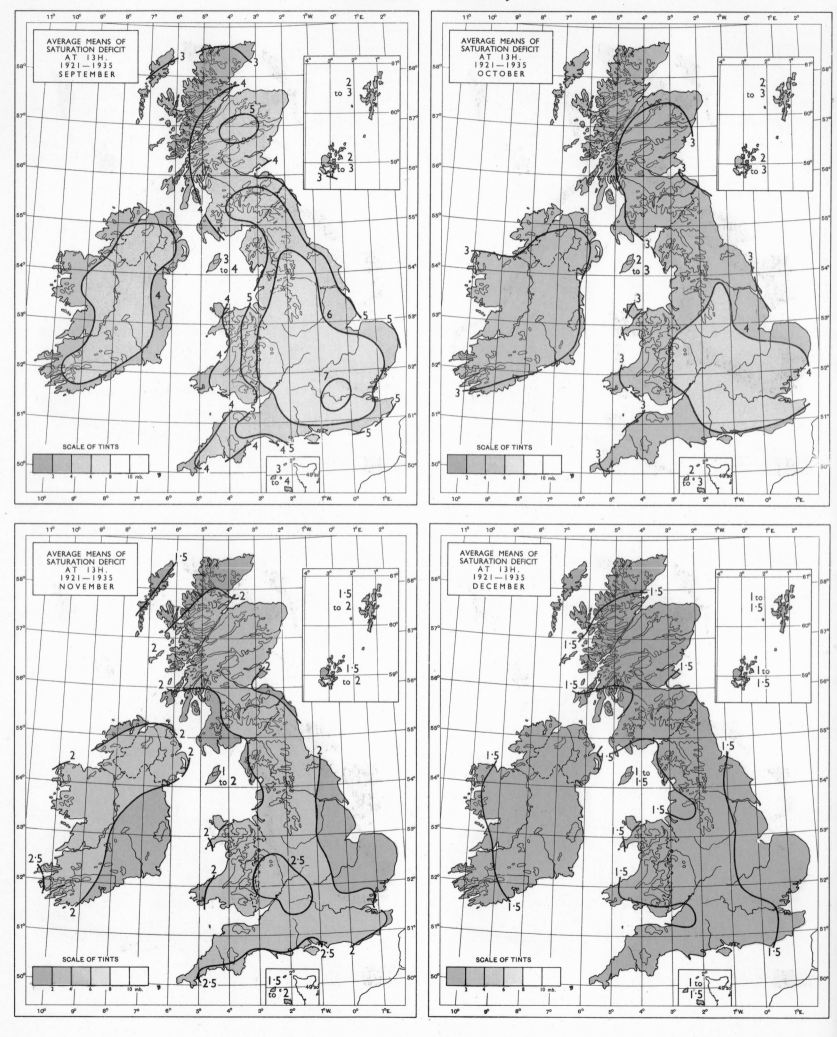

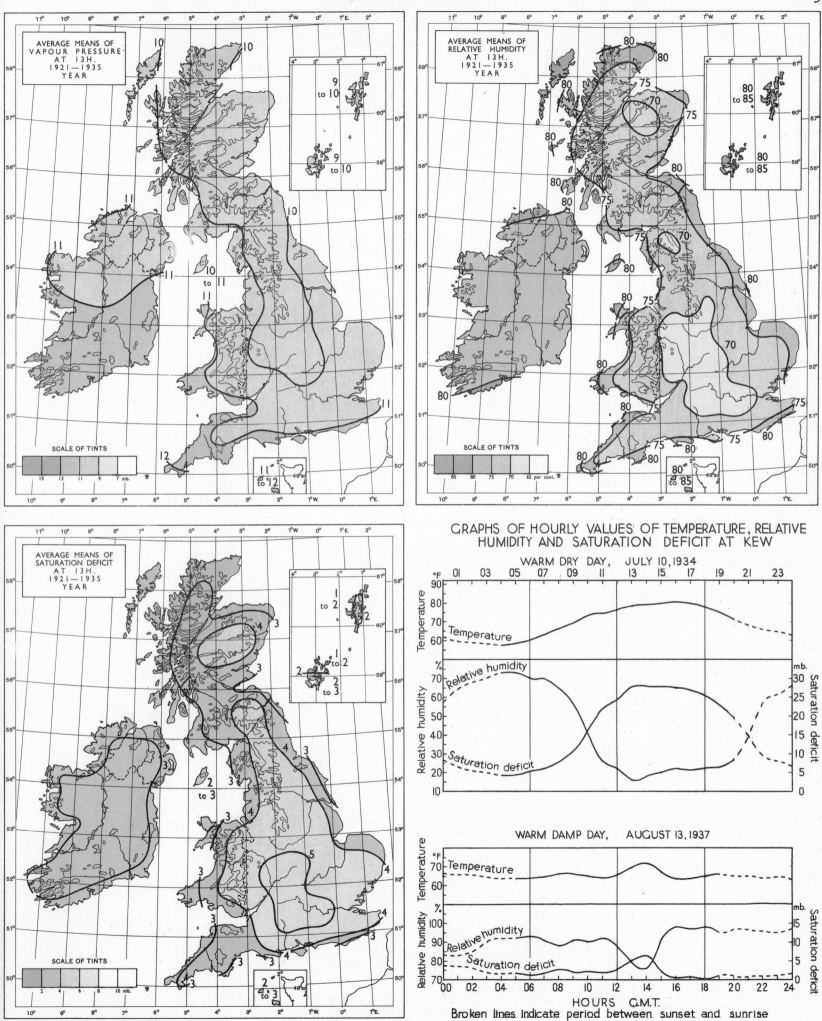

GRAPHS OF HOURLY VALUES OF TEMPERATURE, RELATIVE HUMIDITY AND SATURATION DEFICIT AT KEW

WARM DRY DAY,   JULY 10, 1934

WARM DAMP DAY,   AUGUST 13, 1937

HOURS G.M.T.
Broken lines indicate period between sunset and sunrise

GRAPHS OF AVERAGE HOURLY VAPOUR PRESSURE AND SATURATION DEFICIT

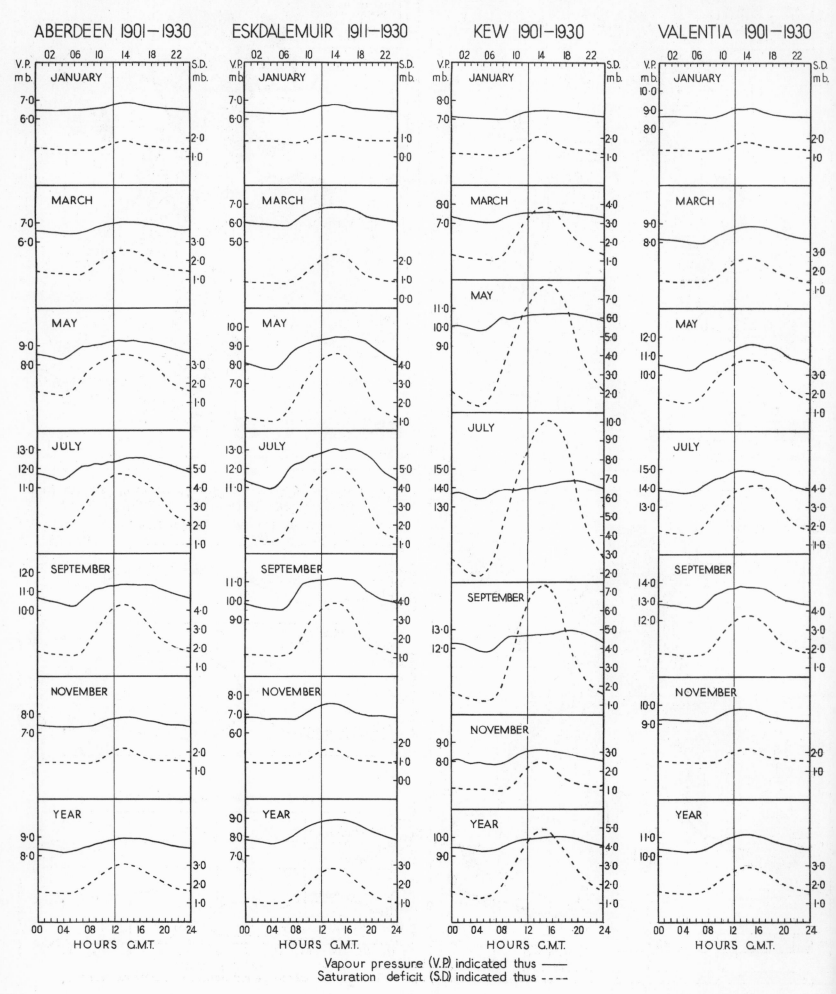

ABERDEEN 1901—1930　　ESKDALEMUIR 1911—1930　　KEW 1901—1930　　VALENTIA 1901—1930

Vapour pressure (V.P.) indicated thus ———
Saturation deficit (S.D.) indicated thus ----

GRAPHS OF AVERAGE HOURLY RELATIVE HUMIDITY

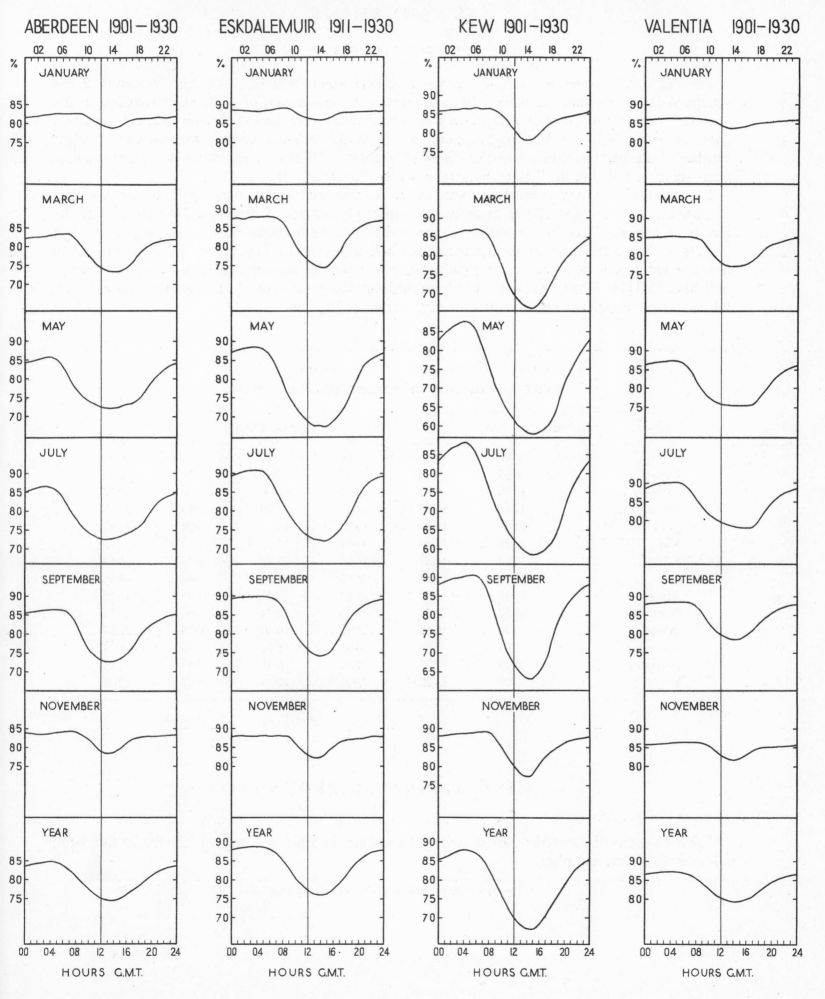

§8—SUNSHINE

INTRODUCTION

The maps and graphs of sunshine are based on data which have been obtained by means of the Campbell-Stokes sunshine recorder. In this instrument the duration of sunshine is recorded in the form of a scorched or burnt line traced on a graduated card by the rays of the sun focussed through a spherical lens. Only sunshine bright enough to scorch the card is recorded, and the term " bright sunshine " is usually used to denote this degree of intensity. Details of the instrument and its management are to be found in the " Meteorological observer's handbook "[1]*.

The averages of sunshine are here expressed as monthly and annual means of the daily duration of sunshine in hours, and also as monthly and annual percentages of the mean daily duration of the possible sunshine. This latter is defined as the interval of time between the ascending and descending transits of the centre of the sun's disc across the horizon, allowance being made for refraction. The monthly and annual values of the mean daily duration of possible sunshine, given for every two degrees of latitude in Table I, have been computed from the basic data given in the " International meteorological tables "[2], and are applicable, without appreciable error, to any year.

TABLE I.—DURATION OF POSSIBLE SUNSHINE (HOURS)

| | Latitude (North) | | | | | |
	50°	52°	54°	56°	58°	60°
January	8·55	8·26	7·95	7·60	7·19	6·70
February	10·00	9·85	9·67	9·48	9·26	9·02
March	11·81	11·79	11·77	11·75	11·73	11·70
April	13·69	13·82	13·96	14·11	14·28	14·47
May	15·33	15·60	15·89	16·22	16·60	17·03
June	16·22	16·57	16·96	17·41	17·94	18·59
July	15·81	16·13	16·48	16·88	17·34	17·88
August	14·40	14·59	14·79	15·01	15·26	15·55
September	12·60	12·64	12·69	12·74	12·80	12·86
October	10·73	10·63	10·52	10·40	10·26	10·12
November	9·03	8·80	8·53	8·24	7·90	7·51
December	8·09	7·77	7·40	6·98	6·49	5·93
Year	12·20	12·22	12·23	12·25	12·27	12·30

HISTORICAL BACKGROUND

Extreme Values of Sunshine

Table II shows the recorded values of bright sunshine, maxima and minima, for the British Isles, with details of date and place.

* The superior figures refer to the bibliography on page 118.

TABLE II.—SUNSHINE EXTREMES

Period	Total	Date	Place	Average per day	Percentage of possible
	hr.			hr.	%
		Maxima			
Year	2,340	1893	Jersey	6·41	52·6
	2,158	1911	Eastbourne	5·91	48·3
	2,112	1911	Torquay	5·79	47·4
Month	384·0	July, 1911	Eastbourne, Hastings	12·39	77·6
	383·0	July, 1911	Torquay	12·36	77·8
	372·0	{ June, 1923 / June, 1925	Jersey } / Plymouth }	12·40	{ 77·1 / 76·2
Week	105·4	June 2-8, 1940	Colwyn Bay	15·06	91·6
Day	17·1	June 14, 1920	Deerness	..	93·7
	15·8	June 13, 1887	Kew	..	95·9
	15·4	July 6, 1941	Ross-on-Wye	..	93·5
		Minima			
Year	1,101	1912	Cullompton	3·02	24·7
Month	0·3	December, 1890	Kew	0·01	0·12
	0·3	December, 1912	Manchester	0·01	0·13
	0·5	December, 1936	Fort William	0·02	0·24

PLATES 1-7

MAPS OF AVERAGE MONTHLY AND ANNUAL MEANS OF DAILY DURATION OF BRIGHT SUN-SHINE AND OF PERCENTAGE OF POSSIBLE BRIGHT SUNSHINE, 1901-1930.—The maps are based on the figures published in "Averages of bright sunshine for the British Isles "[3]. At a considerable number of stations observations are available for the full period of 30 years, 1901-1930. At others the period covered was shorter and when plotting the charts the values at short-period stations were marked so that in drawing the isopleths less weight could be given to them. To make the network of stations still closer, values were computed for stations starting more recently by weighting them with values at near-by stations[4].

GRAPHS OF AVERAGE HOURLY DURATION OF BRIGHT SUNSHINE AT FOUR OBSERVATORIES.— These graphs show the average hourly duration of bright sunshine for the six alternate months January, March, May, July, September and November, and also for the year. The period covered for Aberdeen, Kew and Valentia is 1901-1930, and for Eskdalemuir 1911-1930. Times of sunrise and sunset on the first and last days of the month are shown on the graphs by vertical pecked lines.

PLATE 8

MAPS OF AVERAGE ANNUAL NUMBER OF DAYS WITH NO BRIGHT SUNSHINE AND OF DAYS WITH MORE THAN NINE HOURS, 1913-1932.—These maps are based on values given in "Averages of bright sunshine for the British Isles "[3]. The data refer to 18 scattered stations; the averages for 14 of these cover the period 1913-1932, and 1921-1932 for the remainder. In order to obtain a closer net-work in the map representing sunless days, use has, in addition, been made of 5-year averages weighted to the standard period. In the map representing days with more than 9 hours, averages for additional stations were calculated from an empirical formula.

There is a marked increase in the number of days with more than 9 hours' sunshine from north to south and from inland to the coast. There is also a decrease from north to south and from inland to the coast in the number of sunless days.

GRAPHS OF MONTHLY PERCENTAGE FREQUENCY OF DAYS WITH MORE THAN 50 PER CENT. OF POSSIBLE BRIGHT SUNSHINE, 1913-1932.—This diagram has been taken from a paper by Bilham and Lewis[5] and represents curves for six selected stations. These are of special interest because the criterion selected, more than 50 per cent. of the possible sunshine, eliminates variations due to latitude and the time of year. The resulting data may be regarded as representing the average frequency with which a certain state of the sky occurs during the period of daylight at the selected stations. Days with more than half the possible duration of bright sunshine are regarded as " sunny " days.

BIBLIOGRAPHY

[1] London, Meteorological Office. Meteorological observer's handbook. London, 1942.

[2] International Meteorological Committee. International meteorological tables. Paris, 1890, p. 52.

[3] London, Meteorological Office. Averages of bright sunshine for the British Isles for periods ending 1930.. London, 1934.

[4] GLASSPOOLE, J. and HANCOCK, D. S. ; The distribution over the British Isles of the average duration of bright sunshine. *Quart. J.R. met. Soc., London*, **62**, 1936, p. 247.

[5] BILHAM, E. G. and LEWIS, L. F. ; The frequency of days with specified duration of bright sunshine. *Prof. notes met. Off., London*, **5**, No. 69, 1935.

BRODIE, F. J. ; The incidence of bright sunshine over the United Kingdom during the thirty years, 1881-1910. *Quart. J.R. met. Soc., London*, **42**, 1916, p. 23.

BROOKS, C. E. P. ; The relation between the duration of bright sunshine registered by a Campbell-Stokes sunshine recorder and the estimated amount of cloud. *Prof. notes met. Off., London*, **4**, No. 53, 1929.

CURTIS, R. H. ; Hourly variation of sunshine at seven stations in the British Isles, 1881-1890. *Quart. J.R. met. Soc., London*, **21**, 1895, p. 216.

HANCOCK, D. S. ; General sunshine values, England and Wales, Scotland, Ireland, and the British Isles for the period 1909-1933. *Quart. J.R. met. Soc., London*, **61**, 1935, p. 45.

London, Meteorological Office. The book of normals of meteorological elements for the British Isles for periods ending 1915. Section III, Maps of the normal distribution of temperature, rainfall and sunshine. London, 1920.

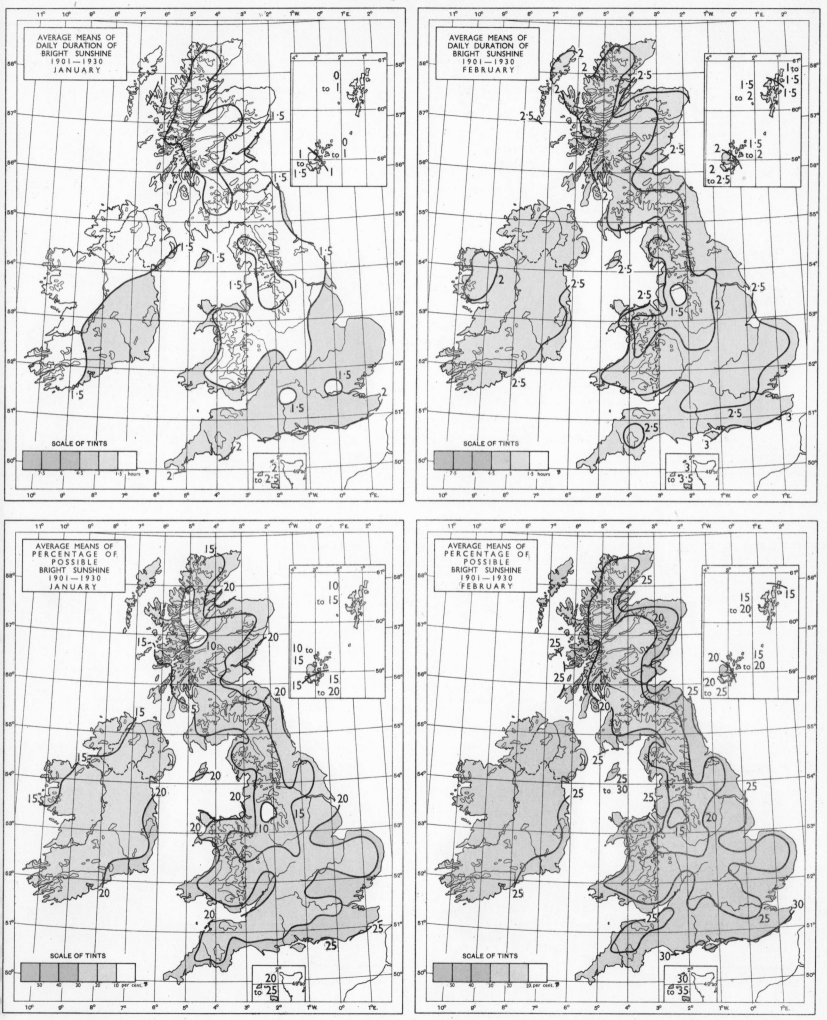

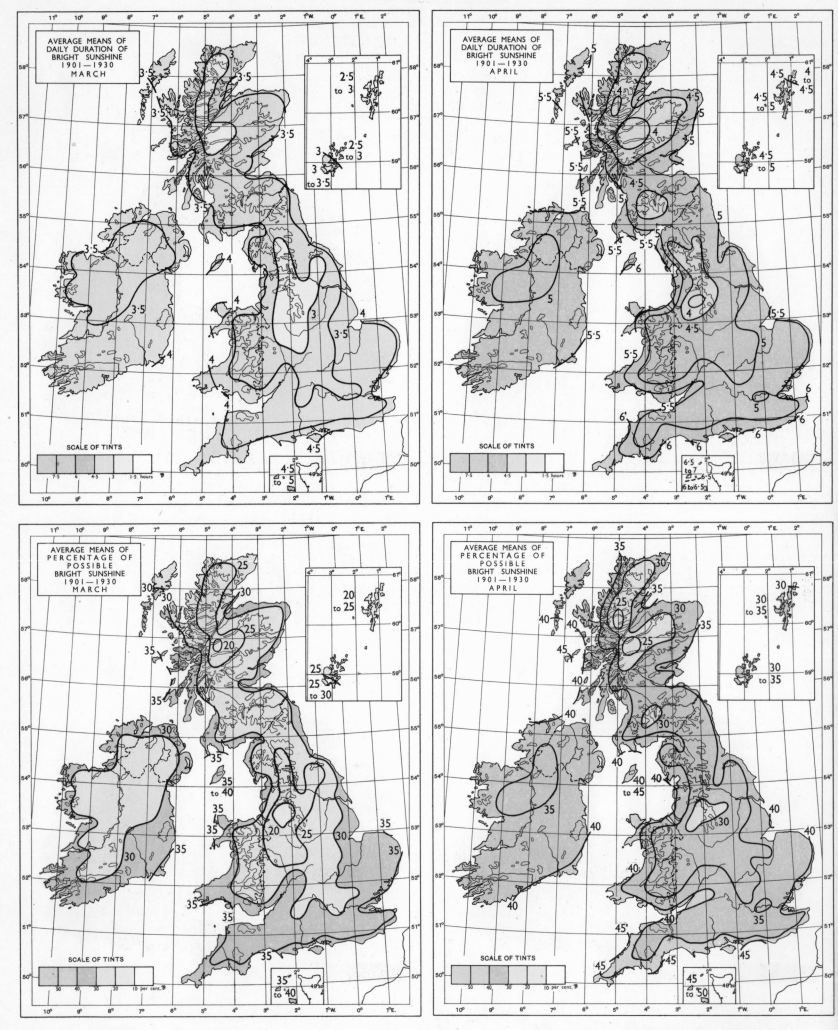

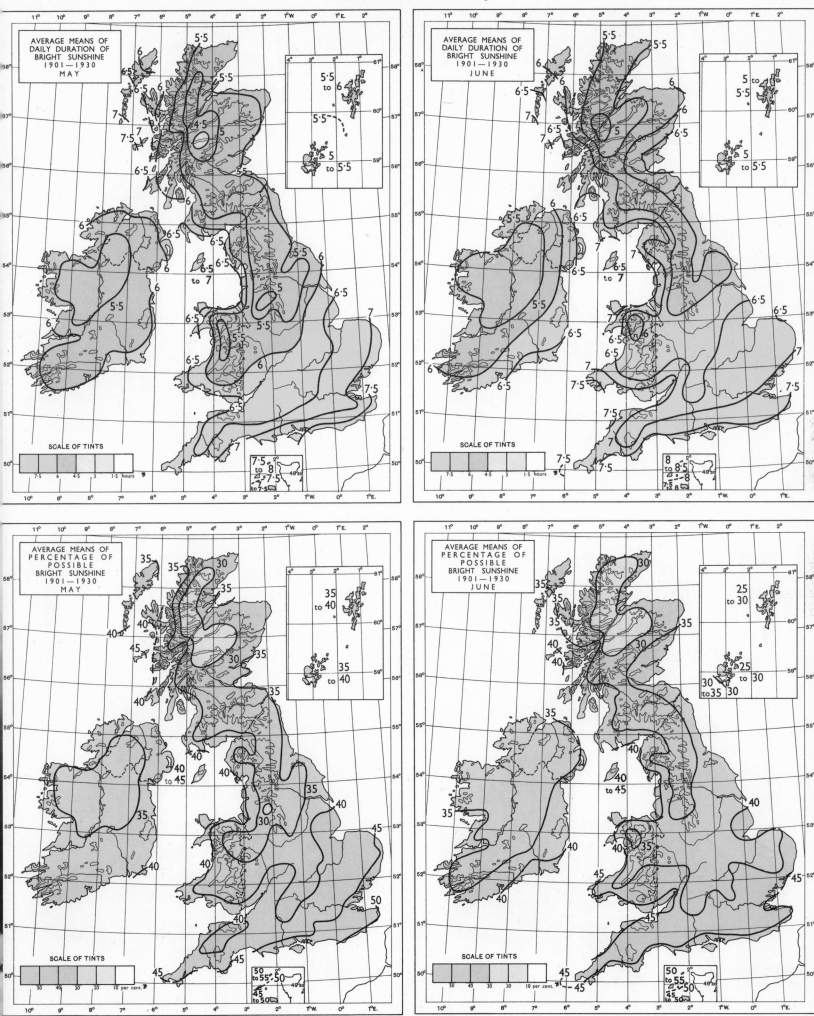

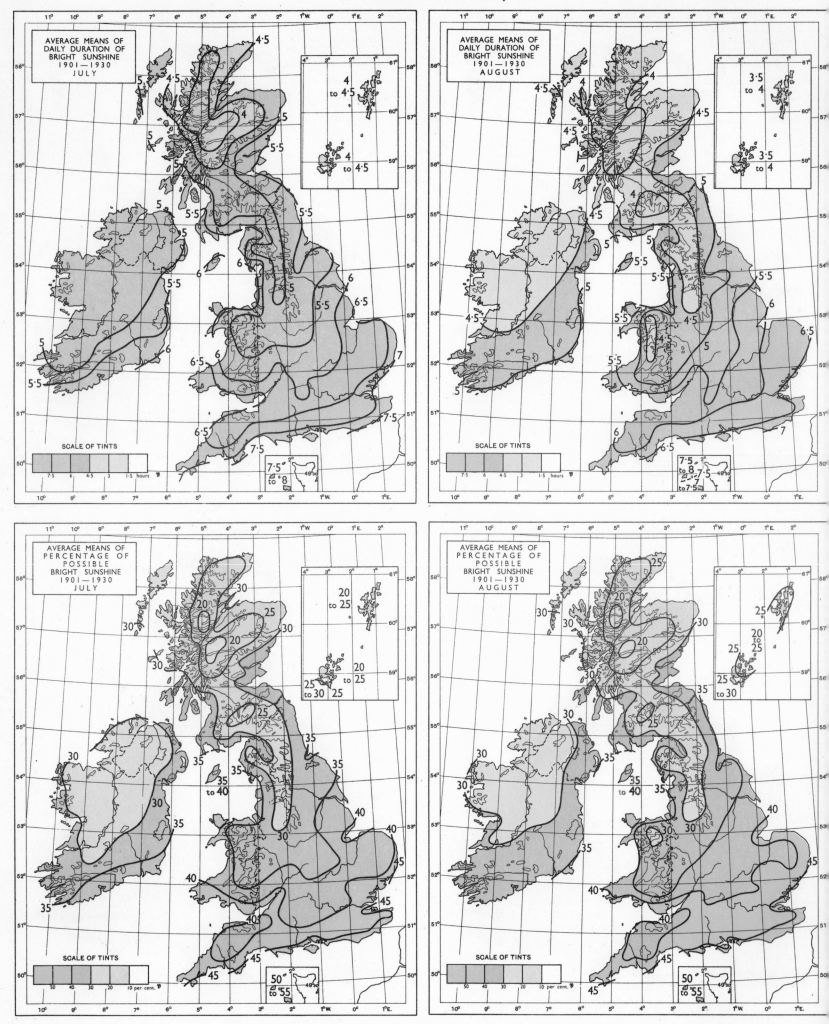

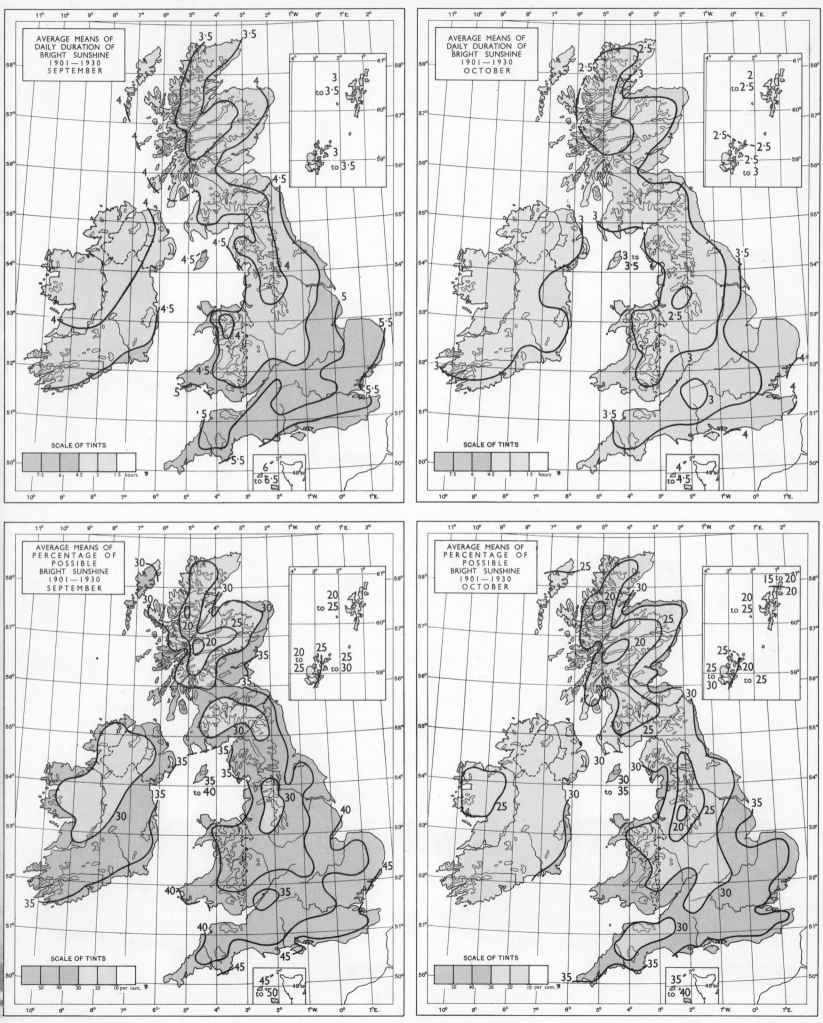

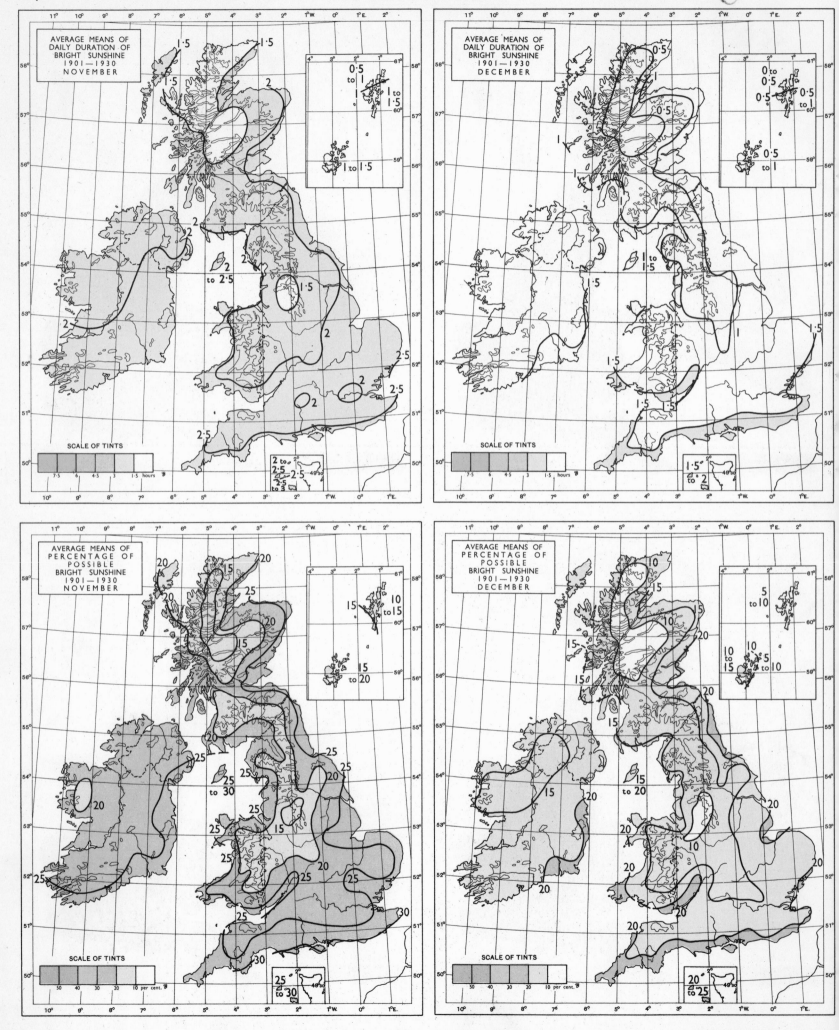

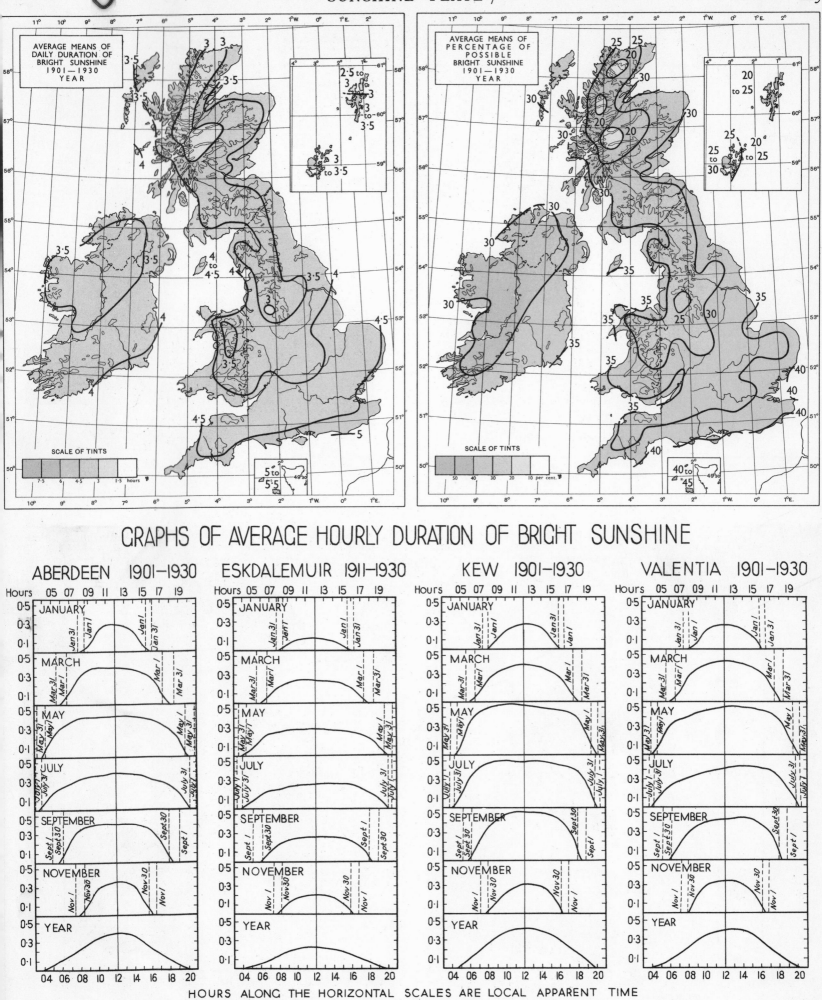

GRAPHS OF AVERAGE HOURLY DURATION OF BRIGHT SUNSHINE

HOURS ALONG THE HORIZONTAL SCALES ARE LOCAL APPARENT TIME

The times of sunrise and sunset for the dates given are indicated by vertical broken lines

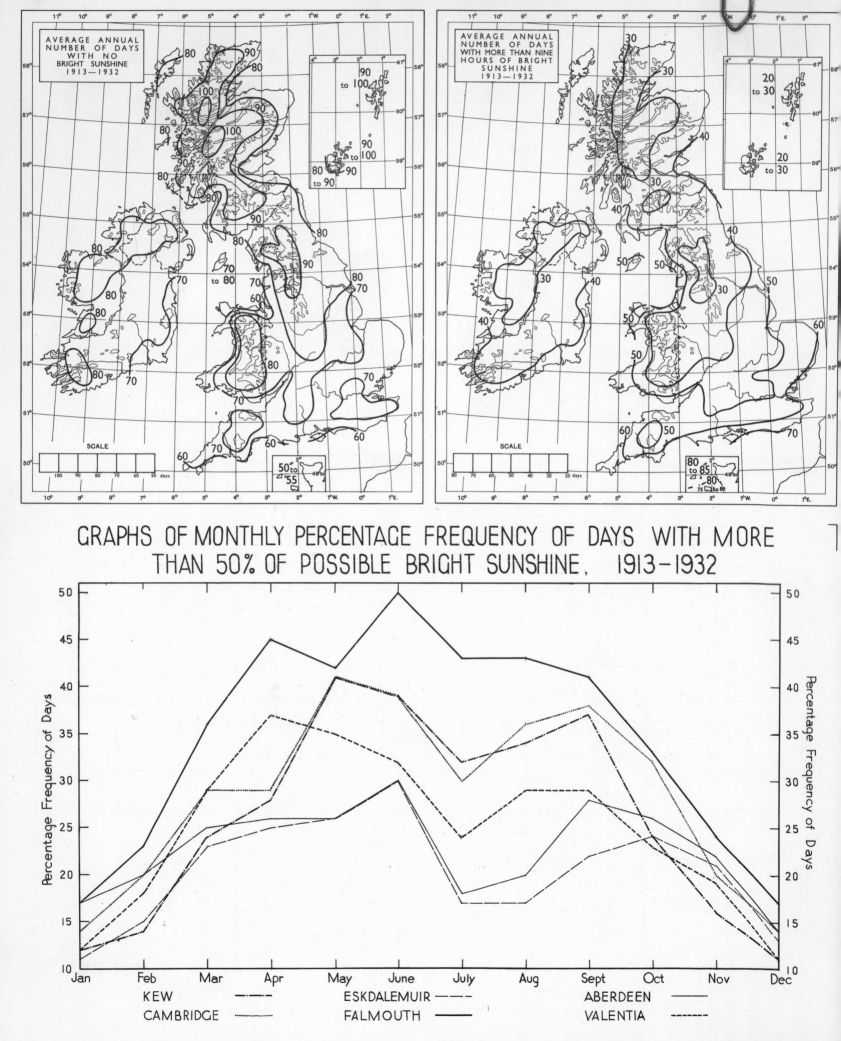

GRAPHS OF MONTHLY PERCENTAGE FREQUENCY OF DAYS WITH MORE
THAN 50% OF POSSIBLE BRIGHT SUNSHINE, 1913–1932

§9—FOG AND VISIBILITY

INTRODUCTION

Since 1921 the range of visibility in a horizontal direction has been regarded as an important meteorological element. To measure the horizontal visibility during the day-time the observer looks at suitable objects chosen at standard distances from the observing station and notes the distance of the furthest object which can just be seen at the time of observation and recognised for what it is. At night it is necessary to use a visibility meter. An instrument[1]* is used in conjunction with a light placed at a certain distance, the obscurity in the atmosphere being supplemented artificially by means of light filters within the instrument until the light, as viewed through it, is just extinguished. Care is taken to ensure that the night observations are strictly comparable with the day-time ones. Full instructions concerning the selection of visibility objects and the methods of observation and recording are contained in the " Meteorological observer's handbook "[2].

To each visibility object is assigned a letter of the alphabet (A to M), and in turn these letters are grouped under the figures 0 to 9, where 0 denotes " dense fog " and 9 " exceptional visibility." It is these ten categories which are used for summarising visibility data. The letters, figures, description and standard distances are set out at the foot of Plate 4.

PLATES 1 AND 2

MAPS OF AVERAGE SEASONAL AND ANNUAL NUMBER OF OCCASIONS OF VISIBILITY 6¼ MILES OR MORE AT 13H., 1927-1938.—These maps are based on observations made at 63 stations, and therefore cannot show more than the broad features of the geographical distribution. Averages for those stations whose records covered only part of the period have been adjusted.

PLATES 2 AND 3

MAPS FOR THE YEAR AND FOR THE SUMMER AND WINTER OF THE AVERAGE NUMBER OF OCCASIONS OF FOG (VISIBILITY LESS THAN 1,100 YARDS); MAPS FOR THE YEAR AND FOR THE WINTER OF THE AVERAGE NUMBER OF OCCASIONS OF THICK FOG (VISIBILITY LESS THAN 220 YARDS); AT 9H., 1934-1943.—The large variation in fog frequency at 9h. in the few regions where observation stations are relatively close together shows that in general there are not enough to allow isopleths to be drawn with any approach to accuracy. The most that can be hoped from them is that they may bring out some of the broadest features of the geographical distribution. The frequencies at the few observation stations more than 500 feet above sea level, of which there are nine in England, two in Wales and nine in Scotland, are apt to be very different from those for neighbouring stations at lower levels, doubtless because a large proportion of fogs at high levels is due to low cloud whereas most of those in the valleys are due to cooling by radiation or to industrial smoke, or to a combination of the two.

It is impossible to deduce even the approximate run of the isopleths at high levels because the number of stations available, namely 20, is too small and none of them is situated as high as 1,500 feet. Hence all stations above 500 feet have been ignored in drawing the isopleths, which are therefore meaningless where they pass over ground above 500 feet. Had the number of observations available at high levels been sufficient to enable isopleths to be drawn in detail, there is little doubt that in the western parts of the Welsh and Scottish hills, above about 1,000 feet, the isopleths would have followed roughly the

---

*The superior figures refer to the bibliography on page 131.

contour lines since increased height generally means increased frequency of immersion in low cloud in such regions. It may be noted that, below 500 feet, elevation alone is no guide to fog frequency, although there is every reason for regarding the contours of the surrounding country as having importance in that they influence local winds and weather. Table I illustrates to some extent this point, but to appreciate it fully it is necessary to note also that the individual values for each interval of height show a high degree of scatter, the highest being sometimes twenty or even thirty times as great as the lowest.

TABLE I.—TOTAL NUMBER OF OCCASIONS OF FOG (VISIBILITY LESS THAN 1,100 YARDS) AT 9H. IN WINTER (OCTOBER-MARCH) IN ENGLAND AND WALES, 1934-1943

Height above M.S.L. in feet	0–100	101–200	201–300	301–400	401–500
Inland south of lat. 53° ...	207	270	189	157	193
Inland north of lat. 53° ...	254	268	278	261	230
Coasts south of lat. 53° ...	89	90	92	..	..
Coasts north of lat. 53° ...	138	152	..	..	..

The apparent maximum for 101-200 feet in the first row of figures is due partly to the fact that three very smoky places—Greenwich, Enfield and Sutton Bonnington—happen to be within this range of height. Without these the mean would only have been 236.

It was found, when drawing the isopleths, that the figures in a few cases appeared to be consistently too large or too small even after allowance had been made for any likely causes for abnormality. In such cases the figures were ignored as it seemed undesirable to introduce considerable distortion of the isopleths, or even to add one or more isopleths on the unsupported evidence of a single station. In some of these cases, possibly even in all, the figures may be substantially correct and represent a real local variation. It therefore seems desirable to record the station names. Those with more fogs than would be expected in view of the figures for neighbouring stations include Stirling, Redcar, Aberystwyth, Mursley, Addington Hills, Walton-on-the-Naze, Halstead, Wakehurst, Tintagel, Exmouth and Seaton. Those with fewer than expected include Keswick, Castleton, Leicester, Tunbridge Wells and Penzance.

The relative lack of fog in summer is exaggerated because, in this season, 9h. is so long after sunrise that fog, which has formed in the night, has often dispersed by then. For this reason the average figure very rarely exceeds five, and over most of the country is less than one for the four summer months, at that hour. At 7h. the figures are higher, as can be seen from Table II, and would doubtless be higher still at about sunrise.

TABLE II.—AVERAGE NUMBER OF OCCASIONS OF FOG (VISIBILITY LESS THAN 1,100 YARDS) AT 7H. IN SUMMER (MAY-AUGUST), 1934-1943

Stations below 500 feet

Lerwick	7	Manchester (Barton)	(13)	Bristol (Whitchurch)	(3)
Stornoway	1	Rotherham	(9)	Boscombe Down ...	(8)
Wick	8	Cranwell	7	South Farnborough ...	4
Aberdeen	4	Spurn Head	7	Kew	2
Tiree	2	Gorleston	3	Croydon	3
Glasgow (Abbotsinch)	3	Birmingham (Edgbaston)	7	Lympne	4
Leuchars	3	Sutton Bonnington ...	(10)	Manston	(2)
St. Abb's Head ...	(9)	Mildenhall	(4)	Scilly	9
Point of Ayr	(2)	St. Ann's Head ...	9	Lizard Head	11
Tynemouth	6	Ross-on-Wye ...	5	Plymouth (Mt. Batten)	3
Catterick	6	Shoeburyness... ...	2	Portland Bill	3
Holyhead	(3)	Hartland Point ...	(6)	Calshot	(2)
Sealand	4			Dungeness	4

Brackets indicate that the record has been completed from neighbouring stations.

Although there is inadequate material from which to study the diurnal variation of fog, the figures in Tables III and IV suffice to show that it differs very much in different places and is not the same in summer as it is in winter.

TABLE III.—TOTAL NUMBER OF OCCASIONS OF FOG (VISIBILITY LESS THAN 1,100 YARDS) AND OF THICK FOG (VISIBILITY LESS THAN 220 YARDS) IN WINTER (OCTOBER-MARCH), 1934-1943

Station	Fog					Thick Fog				
	1h.	7h.	13h.	18h.	21h.	1h.	7h.	13h.	18h.	21h.
Lerwick	5	15	5	8	ø	1	0	0	3	ø
Stornoway...	1	5	1	1	ø	0	1	1	0	ø
Aberdeen	ø	56	47	101	69	ø	8	1	6	4
Eskdalemuir	ø	99	41	60	64	ø	30	16	16	14
Tynemouth	59	65	111	74	ø	4	5	4	4	ø
Spurn Head	116	143	113	104	ø	56	62	34	40	ø
Yarmouth...	66	112	70	65	ø	23	48	14	20	ø
St. Ann's Head	49	52	45	37	ø	31	29	16	28	ø
Kew	ø	269	174	166	212	ø	141	36	39	72
Croydon	224	229	169	284	ø	53	76	36	43	ø
Scilly	53	45	38	45	ø	16	9	3	9	ø
Portland Bill	24	33	25	22	ø	3	2	1	1	ø

ø No observation.

TABLE IV.—TOTAL NUMBER OF OCCASIONS OF FOG (VISIBILITY LESS THAN 1,100 YARDS) AND OF THICK FOG (VISIBILITY LESS THAN 220 YARDS) IN SUMMER (MAY-AUGUST), 1934-1943

Station	Fog					Thick Fog				
	1h.	7h.	13h.	18h.	21h.	1h.	7h.	13h.	18h.	21h.
Lerwick	68	67	29	37	ø	49	43	13	18	ø
Stornoway...	13	10	3	5	ø	4	3	1	1	ø
Aberdeen	ø	39	10	14	32	ø	2	1	0	2
Eskdalemuir	ø	45	8	9	22	ø	7	1	5	8
Tynemouth	41	63	27	9	ø	6	10	5	9	ø
Spurn Head	37	65	13	27	ø	21	20	3	13	ø
Yarmouth...	20	29	8	11	ø	6	8	1	3	ø
St. Ann's Head	78	87	47	50	ø	52	54	24	33	ø
Kew	ø	24	1	2	4	ø	8	0	0	0
Croydon	21	25	1	4	ø	3	4	0	0	ø
Scilly	84	86	36	35	ø	28	30	4	10	ø
Portland Bill	26	35	28	33	ø	2	1	0	3	ø

ø No observation.

As it is not possible to draw isopleths of fog frequency for stations above 500 feet, the monthly totals in ten years for such stations are shown in Table V together with their heights.

TABLE V.—TOTAL NUMBER OF OCCASIONS OF FOG (VISIBILITY LESS THAN 1,100 YARDS) AT 9H., 1934-1943

Stations above 500 feet

Station	Height	Jan.	Feb.	Mar.	Apr.	May	June	July	Aug.	Sept.	Oct.	Nov.	Dec.	Year
	ft.				*England and Wales*									
Princetown	1,359	129	106	92	57	44	40	65	50	62	76	99	82	902
Cantref	1,080	31	32	28	12	4	5	6	11	8	19	13	20	189
Buxton	1,007	96	74	56	23	12	8	6	12	29	36	55	79	486
Bellingham	849	13	15	15	12	5	1	0	2	8	9	12	12	104
Huddersfield (Oakes) ...	761	82	57	82	41	28	19	16	32	41	52	59	60	569
Rhayader	757	16	12	17	3	0	(0)	(0)	(3)	(11)	(21)	(17)	36	(136)
Darwen	724	70	46	43	17	6	7	4	8	24	44	54	83	406
Bingley	610	(67)	(50)	(52)	(21)	(18)	14	3	23	30	44	52	62	(436)
Market Drayton	581	(70)	(51)	(47)	(17)	(10)	(4)	(12)	(14)	(28)	(52)	(62)	(61)	(428)
Newton Rigg	560	7	2	6	2	0	2	1	1	2	2	14	11	50
Meltham	514	(47)	(30)	(56)	(23)	(22)	(10)	(9)	(21)	(29)	(30)	(53)	(26)	(356)
					Scotland									
Braemar	1,111	3	0	3	0	2	0	0	0	1	1	6	1	17
West Linton	820	96	80	78	29	24	25	22	33	41	53	57	73	611
Dungavel	798	16	13	11	7	3	0	3	9	4	8	17	22	113
Balerno	750	13	8	20	10	9	6	10	9	12	3	7	16	123
Boghall	639	(9)	(8)	(20)	(12)	(11)	(10)	(19)	(13)	(6)	(4)	(9)	(10)	(131)
Logie Coldstone	608	(2)	(0)	(1)	(6)	(6)	(1)	(1)	(0)	(0)	(1)	(0)	(0)	(18)
Wolfelee	537	11	2	4	1	2	7	3	9	8	8	7	8	70
Carluke	534	(13)	(5)	(9)	(2)	(0)	(0)	(1)	(1)	(1)	(6)	(11)	(12)	(61)
Peebles	525	(6)	(0)	(1)	(3)	(0)	(1)	(0)	(0)	(3)	(3)	(9)	(3)	(29)

Brackets indicate that the record has been completed from neighbouring stations.

MAP OF PERCENTAGE FREQUENCY OF FOG (VISIBILITY LESS THAN 1,100 YARDS) AT 9H. IN THE LONDON AREA, SEPTEMBER 1, 1936 TO MARCH 31, 1937.—This map aims at representing the distribution of fog in the London area at 9h., and is based on data given by Durst[3] which cover the periods January to March 1936 and September 1936 to March 1937. In order to fill in detail additional fog data for the area were obtained from Lempfert[4], from visibility observations at London aerodromes for the years 1914-1918, and from records concerning the operation of fog signals in the mouth of the Thames. Use was also made of articles in the *Meteorological magazine*[5, 6, 7], and of notes recorded by motorists concerning roads in the London area which were either notoriously foggy or usually clear of fog.

The final map represents, in as much detail as practicable, the percentage frequency of fog in the winter months of 1936-1937. Comparable data for ten-year periods (mostly about 1925-1934) are available for eight stations. At the urban stations Greenwich, Kensington, Croydon and Kew, the ten-year means average about one-and-a-half times the values for 1936-1937, but at the rural stations Byfleet, Biggin Hill, Rothamsted and Shoeburyness there are no marked or systematic differences between the periods.

PLATE 4

DIAGRAMS OF AVERAGE SEASONAL PERCENTAGE FREQUENCIES OF VISIBILITY RANGES 0 TO 9 AT SELECTED STATIONS AT 7H., 1927-1936.—These diagrams are based on the data published in " Percentage frequencies of various visibility ranges at certain places in the British Isles, 1927-1936 "[8], which contains such frequencies for 49 stations at 7, 13 and 18h. for the months, seasons and the year.

BIBLIOGRAPHY

[1] GOLD, E. ; A practical method of determining the visibility number, V, at night.   *Quart. J. R. met. Soc., London,* **65,** 1939, p. 139.

[2] London, Meteorological Office.   Meteorological observer's handbook.   London, 1942.

[3] DURST, C. S. ; Winter fogs and mist investigation, 1936-1937.   Meteorological Office, London, 1940.

[4] LEMPFERT, R. G. K. ; Report of meteorological council on occurrence and distribution of fog in London, winter 1901-1902 and 1902-1903.   Meteorological Office, London, 1904.

[5] FAIRGRIEVE, J. ; London fog, January 20, 1927.   *Met. Mag., London,* **62,** 1927, p. 29.

[6] FAIRGRIEVE, J. ; London fog, February 21, 1928.   *Met. Mag., London,* **63,** 1928, p. 38.

[7] FAIRGRIEVE, J. ; Fog of January 21, 1930.   *Met. Mag., London,* **65,** 1930, p. 41.

[8] London, Meteorological Office.   Percentage frequencies of various visibility ranges at certain places in the British Isles between the years 1927 and 1936.   London, 1949.

DIXON, F. E. ; Fog on the mainland and coasts of Scotland.   *Prof. notes met. Off., London,* **6,** No. 88, 1939.

ENTWISTLE, F. ; Fog.   *J.R. aero. Soc., London,* **32,** 1928, p. 346.

ENTWISTLE, F. ; The annual and seasonal variations of fog at certain stations in England.   *Prof. notes met. Off., London,* **3,** No. 33, 1923.

London, Air Ministry.   The annual and seasonal distribution of fog in the British Isles and surrounding seas.   London, 1918.

SCOTT, R. H. ; Fifteen years' fogs in the British Isles, 1876-1890.   *Quart. J.R. met. Soc., London,* **19,** 1893, p. 229.

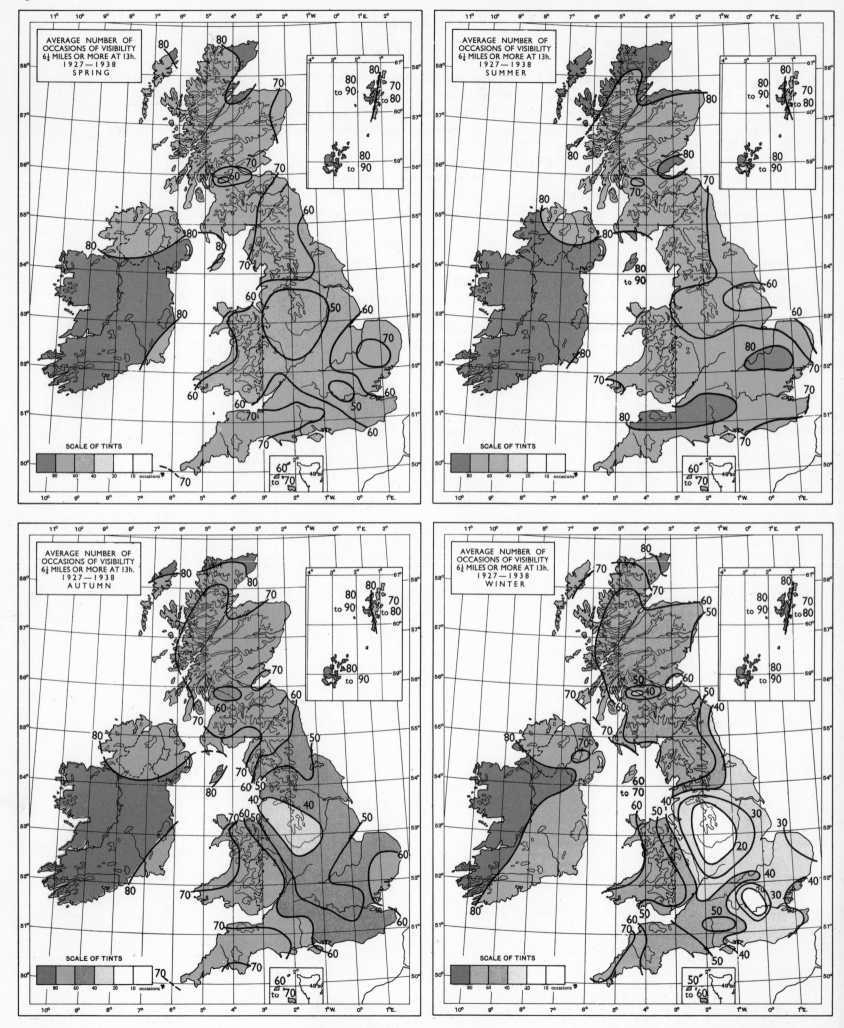

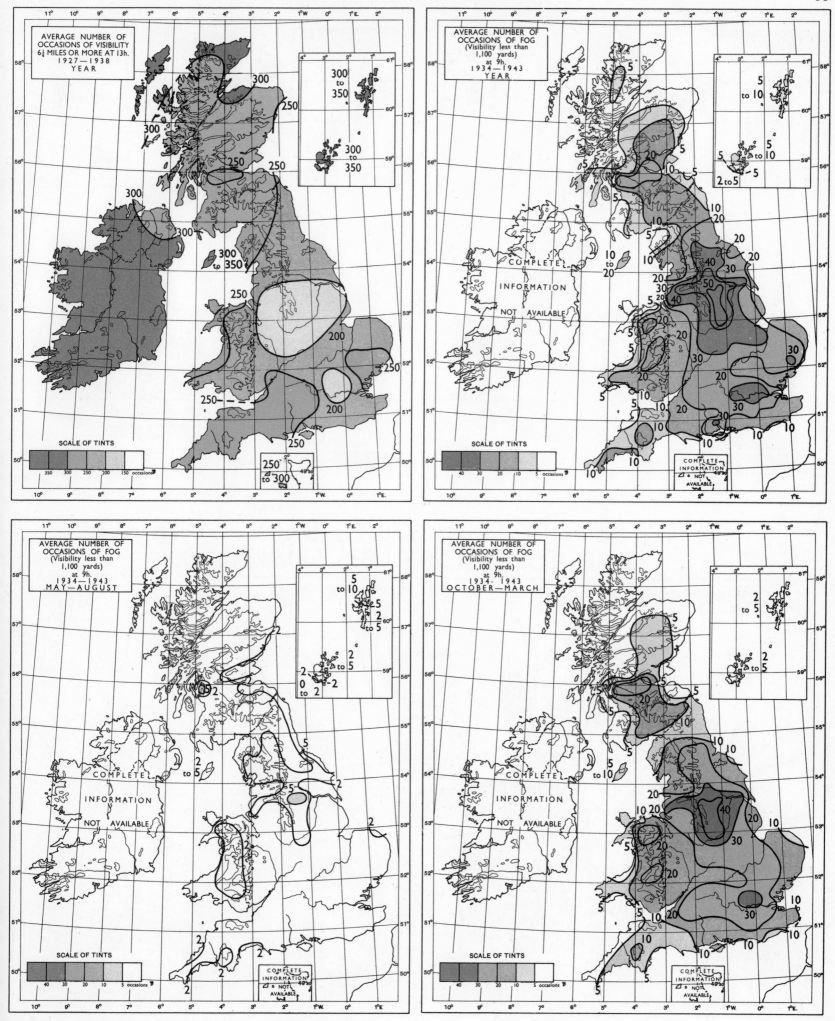

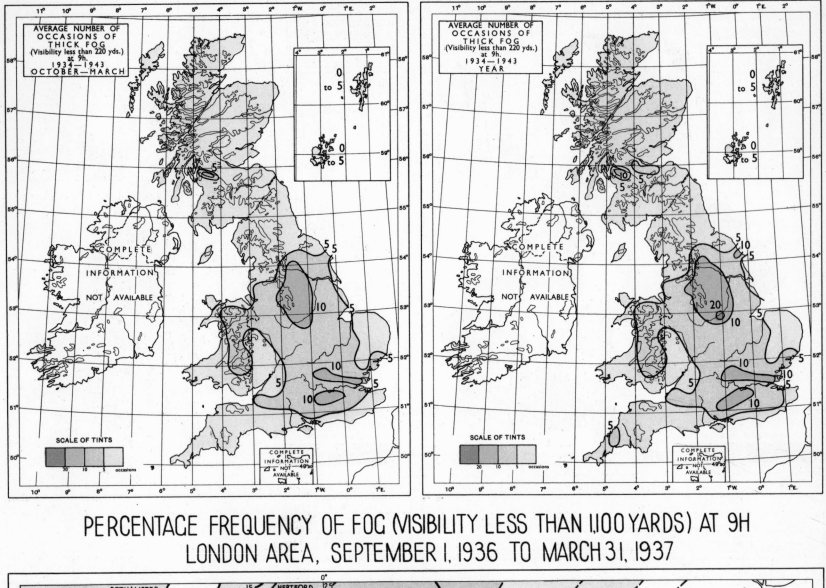

PERCENTAGE FREQUENCY OF FOG (VISIBILITY LESS THAN 1,100 YARDS) AT 9H LONDON AREA, SEPTEMBER 1, 1936 TO MARCH 31, 1937

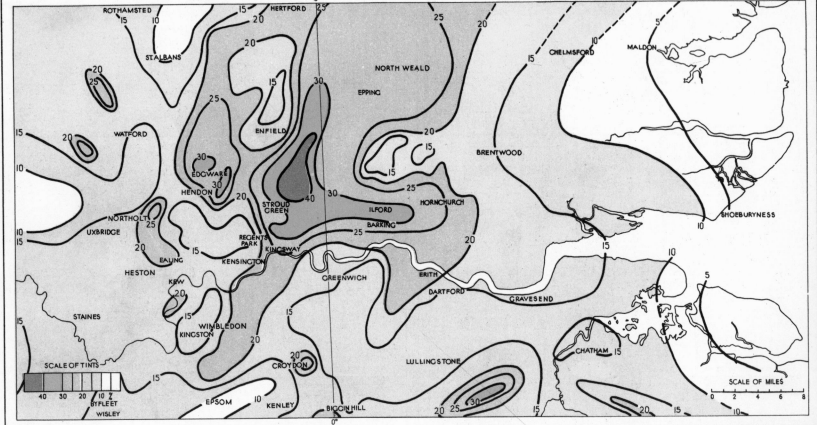

AVERAGE SEASONAL PERCENTAGE FREQUENCIES OF VISIBILITY RANGES 0 TO 9 AT 7H., 1927-1936

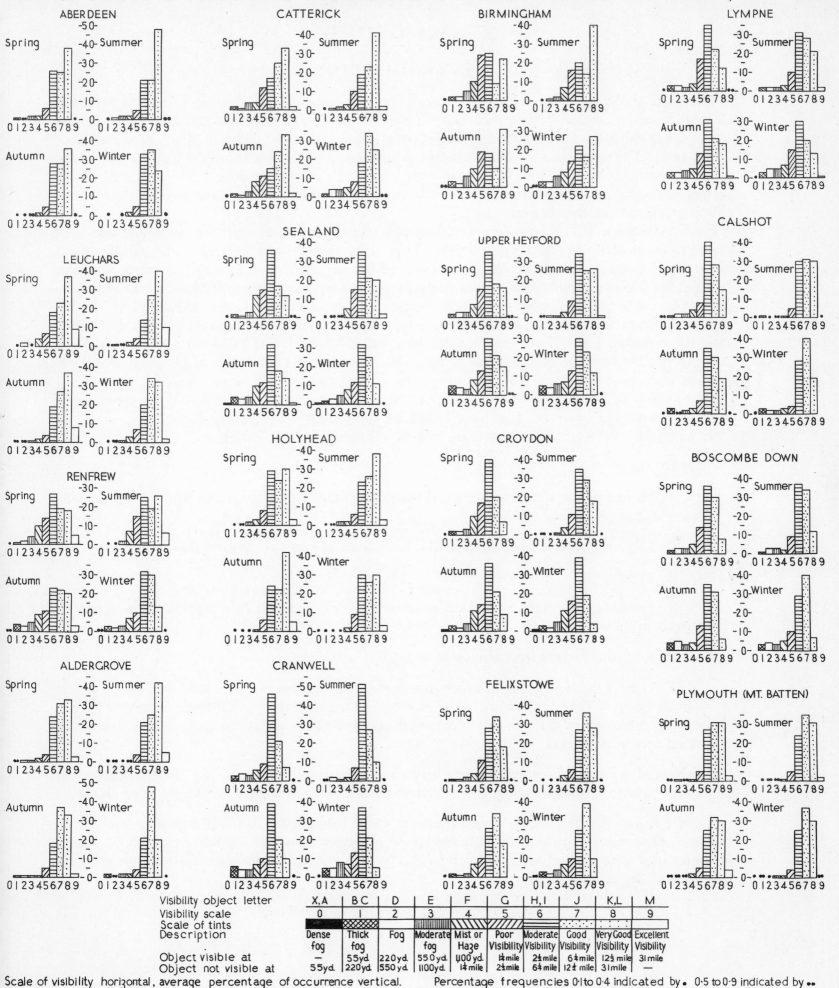

Visibility object letter	X,A	B C	D	E	F	G	H,I	J	K,L	M
Visibility scale	0	1	2	3	4	5	6	7	8	9
Scale of tints										
Description	Dense fog	Thick fog	Fog	Moderate fog	Mist or Haze	Poor Visibility	Moderate Visibility	Good Visibility	Very Good Visibility	Excellent Visibility
Object visible at	—	55yd.	220yd.	550 yd.	1,100 yd.	1¼ mile	2¼ mile	6¼ mile	12½ mile	31 mile
Object not visible at	55yd.	220yd.	550 yd.	1100yd.	1¼ mile	2¼ mile	6¼ mile	12½ mile	31 mile	—

Scale of visibility horizontal, average percentage of occurrence vertical.   Percentage frequencies 0·1 to 0·4 indicated by • 0·5 to 0·9 indicated by ••

§10—CLOUD

INTRODUCTION

The great variety of cloud forms has through the ages attracted the attention of artists, poets and all other lovers of natural beauty. To Luke Howard[1]* must be given the credit of being the first to name and describe the four fundamental types upon which international classifications have ever since been based. The significance of cloud forms for meteorologists has been acknowledged by the publication of the " International cloud atlas "[2], and since the year 1921 the form, amount and height of the clouds present in the sky have been recorded as an important set of weather observations at all Meteorological Office stations in the British Isles.

Previous sections of this atlas imply certain facts concerning cloud form or cloud amount. For example, the rainfall maps of Section 4 infer the presence of rain-bearing clouds : the sunshine maps of Section 8 similarly include implicitly the cloud which was effective in limiting the bright sunshine. It is not feasible to compile climatological maps directly presenting statistics of cloud forms. The sunshine maps are in effect also maps of daylight average cloud amounts of all forms and heights, except thin cirrus. In the present section, therefore, the emphasis is on cloud height, and here are given tables which show the variation of cloud with respect to the two heights 1,000 feet and 8,000 feet above ground level.

These two heights have been selected because cloud base below 1,000 feet is of particular interest to aviation, and cloud base above 8,000 feet is the state of sky described as " no low cloud."

Instructions for making the observations from which the data used were compiled are contained in the " Meteorological observer's handbook "[3] and are supplemented by " Cloud forms "[4].

In particular, the height of lowest cloud may be obtained in the following ways :—

(a) By day

(i) Measuring the time which a small balloon, inflated with hydrogen to rise at a known rate, takes to disappear in the cloud base.

(ii) Receiving reports from aircrew who have flown through or close to the cloud base.

(b) By night

(i) Measuring the time by balloon as (a)(i) but with a candle in a paper lantern suspended from it to show its position.

(ii) Receiving reports from aircrew as in (a)(ii).

(iii) Using a cloud searchlight, which throws up, from one end of a measured base-line, a bright narrow beam of light to illuminate the low cloud by a spot : the vertical angle between this spot and the other end of the base-line is measured and thus the height of the spot, and the base of the cloud, can be calculated.

Experienced observers can usually give a very good estimate of the height of a cloud, but for these tables only data from stations which had instrumental aids for measuring cloud height were used.

Table I shows the frequencies of occurrence of cloud below 1,000 feet above ground level for 44 stations. Over the country as a whole frequencies were greatest in winter and least in summer. Except in winter they were greater inland at 1h. than at 13h. The annual frequencies showed little variation with time of day or with locality.

---

* The superior figures refer to the bibliography on page 139.

TABLE I.—AVERAGE SEASONAL AND ANNUAL NUMBERS OF OCCASIONS WITH CLOUD BELOW 1,000 FEET ABOVE STATION LEVEL AT 1H. AND 13H., 1939-1944

Station	Height above M.S.L.	Spring		Summer		Autumn		Winter		Year	
		1h.	13h.	1h.	13h.	1h.	13h.	1h.	13h.	1h.	13h.
	ft.										
Sullom	12	17	15	32	20	16	17	10	17	75	69
Alness	63	5	3	9	4	3	2	2	1	19	10
Lossiemouth	21	7	7	10	7	3	8	4	7	24	29
Wick	114	16	17	23	19	11	15	7	12	57	63
Tiree	44	8	17	18	21	13	16	12	22	51	76
Oban	74	7	7	10	7	7	6	7	8	31	28
Wigtown	19	13	11	15	11	10	14	11	19	49	55
Renfrew	30	6	7	10	10	9	12	9	16	34	45
Turnhouse (Edinburgh) ...	112	9	8	9	7	10	9	5	6	33	30
Leuchars	36	12	11	15	9	10	9	8	11	45	40
Montrose	22	12	13	14	10	9	12	7	11	42	46
Thornaby	58	10	5	8	5	7	6	8	10	33	26
Linton-on-Ouse	46	9	7	7	6	10	7	16	17	42	37
Squires Gate (Blackpool)	33	4	7	8	10	8	11	9	13	29	41
Sealand	16	5	6	2	6	4	7	11	16	22	35
Church Fenton	27	9	6	6	6	10	7	16	14	41	33
Hemswell	180	10	9	8	7	13	12	15	19	46	47
Scampton	195	9	10	8	7	11	13	14	17	42	47
Driffield	65	10	8	10	8	11	9	11	16	42	41
Digby	108	10	7	8	7	12	11	16	16	46	41
North Coates	11	9	11	11	11	7	10	9	13	36	45
Penrhos	63	11	10	12	10	7	9	9	15	39	44
Bircham Newton	221	13	11	14	10	11	13	18	22	56	56
Wyton	128	9	10	8	6	11	12	17	20	45	48
Duxford	97	9	8	8	5	12	11	16	18	45	42
Mildenhall	15	8	6	7	4	10	9	15	16	40	35
Pembroke Dock	40	13	15	14	11	11	14	15	19	53	59
Abingdon	210	9	8	8	5	12	11	20	22	49	46
Northolt	121	8	7	8	5	12	12	20	21	48	45
North Weald	327	11	10	11	5	14	13	20	23	56	51
Hornchurch	60	5	8	6	5	12	11	18	21	41	45
Felixstowe	10	8	7	7	3	6	8	12	14	33	32
St. Athan	145	9	9	7	5	7	8	13	17	36	39
Bristol (Whitchurch) ...	209	10	10	7	7	11	10	16	20	44	47
Boscombe Down	414	14	9	14	9	14	15	21	24	63	57
South Farnborough ...	226	10	8	8	6	12	10	20	21	50	45
Kenley	524	15	11	11	6	14	13	23	25	63	55
Detling	530	22	16	19	8	20	17	25	26	86	67
Lympne	341	16	14	15	10	14	17	24	31	69	72
Manston	155	13	12	14	9	13	13	21	25	61	59
St. Eval	345	23	20	25	23	18	20	16	26	82	89
Plymouth (Mt. Batten) ...	86	11	12	15	13	10	13	13	16	49	54
Thorney Island	10	9	10	10	7	7	8	13	16	39	41
Tangmere	53	12	10	13	7	9	9	18	21	52	47

Table II shows the frequencies with which no cloud was observed below 8,000 feet above ground level at 44 stations. The most striking feature is the difference between 1h. and 13h. in all seasons, the frequency at 13h. being less than half that at 1h. and much less than half in summer. This reflects the tendency for low cloud to form during the day and to clear away at night.

TABLE II.—AVERAGE SEASONAL AND ANNUAL NUMBERS OF OCCASIONS WITH NO CLOUD
BELOW 8,000 FEET AT 1H. AND 13H., 1939-1944

Station	Height above M.S.L.	Spring		Summer		Autumn		Winter		Year	
		1h.	13h.	1h.	13h.	1h.	13h.	1h.	13h.	1h.	13h.
	ft.										
Sullom	12	10	4	5	1	6	1	5	1	26	7
Alness	63	14	7	3	1	7	2	11	8	35	18
Lossiemouth	21	14	7	7	2	11	4	14	7	46	20
Wick	114	10	7	7	3	6	5	9	7	32	22
Tiree	44	15	8	15	9	6	4	7	3	43	24
Oban	74	17	7	11	3	5	1	10	4	43	15
Wigtown	19	17	5	12	1	11	1	5	1	45	8
Renfrew	30	14	6	10	3	13	3	12	7	49	19
Turnhouse (Edinburgh) ...	112	17	6	15	8	16	6	16	13	64	33
Leuchars	36	18	8	11	2	17	6	20	9	66	25
Montrose	22	15	7	8	2	14	4	16	7	53	20
Thornaby	58	31	12	24	8	25	8	26	14	106	42
Linton-on-Ouse	46	29	9	22	5	23	7	21	11	95	32
Squires Gate (Blackpool)	33	33	20	19	8	19	9	22	11	93	48
Sealand	16	29	13	22	7	19	5	18	10	88	35
Church Fenton	27	35	11	33	7	29	10	25	17	122	45
Hemswell	180	38	13	28	6	30	9	26	6	122	34
Scampton	195	42	13	31	6	37	10	28	18	138	47
Driffield	65	30	8	21	6	20	8	25	12	96	34
Digby	108	44	15	34	8	35	12	27	17	140	52
North Coates	11	39	16	31	9	34	13	29	17	133	55
Penrhos	63	31	13	19	5	11	3	13	7	74	28
Bircham Newton	221	41	15	34	8	33	9	24	17	132	49
Wyton	128	41	14	38	7	41	12	30	19	150	52
Duxford	97	41	17	32	8	38	10	30	16	141	51
Mildenhall...	15	43	17	30	7	34	8	26	17	133	49
Pembroke Dock	40	39	13	35	5	19	3	17	6	110	27
Abingdon	210	43	17	38	6	35	6	24	14	140	43
Northolt	121	42	18	39	9	37	10	25	13	143	50
North Weald	327	44	17	40	9	39	9	25	13	148	48
Hornchurch	60	42	18	39	10	38	11	25	14	144	53
Felixstowe	10	46	19	42	13	35	12	28	19	151	63
St. Athan	145	25	13	20	5	16	5	14	7	75	30
Bristol (Whitchurch) ...	209	36	14	30	7	27	5	17	8	110	34
Boscombe Down	414	40	16	37	6	37	7	25	12	139	41
South Farnborough ...	226	42	16	41	7	33	8	21	11	137	42
Kenley	524	36	18	37	9	34	9	21	11	128	47
Detling	530	36	15	37	8	33	9	25	13	131	45
Lympne	341	40	19	39	14	33	11	25	14	137	58
Manston	155	42	20	38	13	27	12	23	17	130	62
St. Eval	345	30	13	23	5	15	4	14	5	82	27
Plymouth (Mt. Batten) ...	86	32	12	30	6	20	3	15	7	97	28
Thorney Island	10	41	17	38	8	31	8	26	13	136	46
Tangmere	53	40	18	37	8	37	9	24	14	138	49

The diagram below, which is taken from Yule and Kendall[5], shows the frequency distribution of cloudiness at Greenwich in July for the years 1890-1904. It illustrates the fact that, at inland stations in summer, skies which are half-clouded are markedly less frequent than overcast or nearly clear skies.

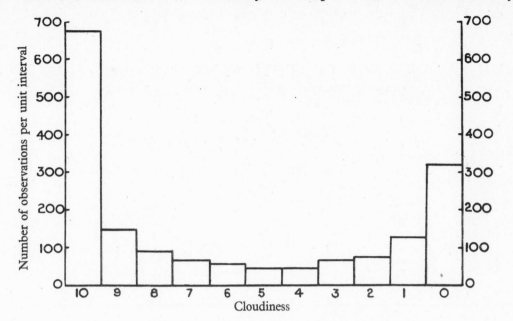

Cloudiness at Greenwich in July; 1,715 observations
Reproduced with permission from " An introduction to the theory of statistics "[5].

BIBLIOGRAPHY

[1] HOWARD, LUKE ; On the modifications of cloud. *Tilloch Phil. Mag., London,* **16,** 1803, pp. 97 and 344 ; **17,** 1803, p. 5.

[2] International Meteorological Committee : Commission for the study of clouds ; International atlas of clouds and of types of the sky. I, General atlas ; II, Nuages tropicaux. Paris, 1932. Abridged edition for the use of observers. Paris, 1930.

[3] London, Meteorological Office. Meteorological observer's handbook. London, 1942.

[4] London, Meteorological Office. Cloud forms according to the international classification. London, 1949.

[5] YULE, G. U. and KENDALL, M. G. ; An introduction to the theory of statistics. London (Charles Griffin & Co.), 1947.

BROOKS, C. E. P. ; The mean cloudiness over the earth. *Mem. R. met. Soc., London,* **1,** No. 10, 1927.

BROOKS, C. E. P. ; The relation between the duration of bright sunshine registered by a Campbell-Stokes sunshine recorder and the estimated amount of cloud. *Prof. notes met. Off., London,* **4,** No. 53, 1929.

CLARKE, G. A. ; Clouds : a descriptive illustrated guide book to the observation and classification of clouds. London (Constable), 1920.

CLAYDEN, A. W. ; Cloud studies. London (John Murray), 1925.

HOGG, W. H. ; Variations in the frequency of clear and cloudy days with the number of observations. *Met. Mag., London,* **76,** 1947, p. 210.

London, Meteorological Office. Percentage frequencies of observations of the height of base of low cloud at certain places in the British Isles between the years 1927 and 1936. London, 1945.

SIMPSON, SIR GEORGE ; On the formation of cloud and rain. *Quart. J.R. met. Soc., London,* **67,** 1941, p. 99.